LUCKY

A NOVEL

BY KRISTINA PARRO

A LOGOS BOOK

AN IMPRINT OF LOGOS LLC
KRISTINAPARRO.COM

Cover Photography: Aleen Olivares, Carl Rupsis
Cover Design (front and back): Kristina Parro
Illustrations: Om Nair
Format/Interior Design: Kristina Parro
Editors: Caitlyn Slawny, Sandra Swinkunas

First U.S. Edition: June 2021
ISBN: 978-1-7369233-2-0 (paperback)
kristinaparro.com
logos@kristinaparro.com

For my Z.

Reality is the ocean; our laws are the ship.
Many have never left the ship, jumped into the sea.
Jump in with me.

ϕ

The universe is made of stories, not atoms.

Muriel Rukeyser, Great American Poet

CHAPTERS

1. Tale As Old As Time
2. Rhea Harmonía
3. The Confederate Soldier
4. Pure Intentions
5. Key to the Dream
6. Nashville
7. Betty West
8. Famous
9. The Bitch Pack
10. Holiday House
11. An American Dynasty
12. The Lucky 1
13. The American Dream
14. Lover
15. Surreal
16. Irrational
17. Legacy
18. Paradox
19. Tragedy
20. Renaissance

PROLOGUE

The date was February 24, 2020. A Monday. I remember it, like it was yesterday. The bright city lights ricocheted off the Edens expressway, blinding me; my Uber headed south, downtown.

Up front, the driver adjusted a dial, and a deep voice filled the back seat. "The Dow drops another thousand points," the radio host boomed, "as fears about the novel Coronavirus grow."

As I peered out the rain-streaked window, I saw a blurry image that has cemented itself in my memory. The driver next to us wore a bright-yellow-full-body hazard suit and was huddled behind the steering wheel. He sat alone in his car; yet had donned elbow-length rubber gloves, and wore a face shield and mask.

What is this? I remember thinking, *the start of a dystopian horror movie?*

Life's funny like that.

I was an essential healthcare worker who worked throughout the pandemic without receiving sick time or hazard pay. People literally sang our praises in the streets, then turned a blind eye as we were stabbed in the back. Along the way, I forgot my value.

My beloved patients caught the virus, one by one. Some died; others were forever changed. Then, I changed, too. I lost my spark.

I felt trapped, like my life was but a marathon on a giant wheel, in the hamster cage that epitomized the tragic reality of our society. I watched as some ran that wheel, round and round, until they died. I watched as others fell off the wheel and never recovered. Maybe some people are just destined for a life at the bottom.

Others, however, are lucky. Barring no pandemics, pay cuts, layoffs, freak weather accidents, or raging forest fires, they may be able to retire and spend their glory years shelling out $20,000 a month to live in a luxury assisted living building.

Take a moment to imagine it with me.

The year is 2069; you are sure of it. That speech therapist who came to your room this morning asked you for the year at least 20 times.

You are elderly now and in the midst of another pandemic.

Your family recently moved you into Thousand Oaks Senior Living. You heard your granddaughter call your new home 'the fancy cruise ship.' The term, quite honestly, suits it well.

Rolling your walker down the padded hallway, you trepidly make your way towards the dining room, barely taking notice of the glistening chandeliers and extravagant art prints. The brakes squeal as you walk distracting you. It's lunchtime, and your stomach feels hollow.

In the dining room, you park your walker by locking the brakes. Taking care not to let gravity win out, you slowly lower yourself into a chair. If you fell, you'd be sent to the hospital. Again.

Going to the hospital is always stressful. Despite working 'til you were 75-years-old and paying extra for the good health insurance, your hospital sent an enormous bill after your last visit.

The next day, you got a notice from the 'cruise ship's' management. Rent is going up next month by 5%. Again.

Wondering, worriedly, you think, *how could my dwindling savings continue to pay the ever increasing cost of living for the rest of my time on Earth?*

Back in the dining room, you see three decrepit acquaintances tucked under the lunch table with you: four forgottens forming a despondent circle. The waiter delivers your meal— turkey pot pie and jello. Again.

You complain, amongst yourselves, about the meal. "So much for the 'gourmet' chef we're paying for," you say, raising a small laugh from one of the others.

Laugh is generous. The sound was more of a chortle; but regardless, any sound of joy is refreshing these days. Meals tend to be melancholy.

Because of the pandemic, the 'cruise ship' isn't allowing any visitors. You haven't seen your family in three months.

The forgottens are depressed. The pandemic is killing them. Four others died just this past week. You hear yourself think, *maybe it's the isolation killing them.*

At the table, talk tends to focus on the weather... it was the safest thing to talk about.

"Gourmet!" Joe, a retired social worker and Veteran, grumbles. His entire left side droops following that stroke he had last year. You notice liquid dribbling out of the side of his mouth as he speaks. "Hmph!"

"The sun is shining real bright out there today," Veronica says. The forgottens look out the window and nod their heads.

Not you, though.

You aren't focused on the table conversation anymore. You're lost in your daydream about this afternoon's main event… *BINGO!*

Later that day, Mary, the director of activities, will sit in the hallway next to the BINGO! generator. Her voice will boom directly into your hearing aids, as she says, "I-21," "B-8," "B-5."

Holographs of letters and numbers will dance across the way, as you try to manage three BINGO! cards from the lawn chair at the entryway of your one-bedroom apartment.

You remember the rush of adrenaline that coursed through your body that first time you yelled, "BINGO!" The prize wasn't memorable; but suddenly you find yourself chasing the thrill of winning, waking up each morning, already thinking towards 3pm. BINGO! gives your daily life a little purpose.

Did that life seem bleak? Don't despair!

Some are luckier, still.

A select few find a way to beat the system and win the game. Winning this game gives you the freedom to live your life on your own terms. A fast pass towards *Happiness House*, the final hurdle before making it to Utopia.

Where better to beat the system than the United States of America?

Many of us can trace our family's history back to when they arrived in this country. Each immigrant made the brave journey in search of the glistening opportunity the Land of Liberty provides. It has become modern folklore; *Your Own Chance at the American Dream.*

The *American Dream* is so appealing because it offers a recipe, of sorts; a clear, fair path that allows anyone the opportunity to unlock the door to a happy life.

I read the stories. I learned from the good examples around me. I knew what to do.

Bad things happen to bad people. Good things happen to good people.

I meandered down the path which I was led towards goodness and happiness. Society taught me— hell, some would even say it told me— if I lived by their rules, their reality, I would find the happiness I sought.

Happiness was all I ever wanted.

But I live in a society dominated by social Darwinism in which the dogma is *feast or be feasted on.*

Here, almost everything has been commoditized in pursuit of limitless growth.

Here, your value as a person is directly correlated with

how you contribute to the growth of your country's GDP[1].

Fun Fact: the industry that makes up Wall Street (finance, insurance, and real estate) accounted for a fifth of the total economy, making it the largest industry by contribution to GDP, according to a 2019 report from the Bureau of Economic Analysis.

At the end of the path society told me to follow, in pursuit of the goals I had been coached to strive for, I didn't find happiness. Instead, I found a cage and a hamster wheel. Then I found myself thrust into a pandemic, working in one of its most devastating hotspots.

Like it had been dropped in the sea, my hamster cage started filling with salty water.

I saw two choices. I could run, or I could fall.

I chose to run.

I ran away on that wheel, terrified to go into work each day, yet feeling as if I had no other choice. Sometimes, it was easier to imagine I was living the life of someone else.

How easy life must be, I thought, as the Coronavirus ravaged my nursing home, *for someone who has the money and power to make things happen; someone who can do or be anything she ever wanted. That girl isn't caged in by anything. She had won the game of life.*

---

1 Gross Domestic Product (GDP) — Sometimes, you hear people referring to GDP as total value added to a country's economy each year; a measure of a country's economic output or production. GDP is used by policy makers to determine whether an economy is contracting or expanding and then take appropriate action.

I wish I were that lucky! I cried, like a baby, going home in my car.

By this time, water was gushing into my hamster cage. I was drowning in my own tears. Furiously, I searched for the escape hatch.

There it was, shining in the murky water in front of me, shimmering and gold. An escape route, a *Hail Mary* play.

My head emerged. I gasped a deep breath in, then plunged back under the water, guided by the light. I made it to the hatch, but found that it was locked. I didn't have the key.

I peered through the keyhole, and by God, I was able to read the story. Here's what they don't tell you, fellow hamster: that story is a tragedy, too.

It seems that, after escaping the cage trapping us mere mortals, there's another game. The end game is called the *Pursuit of Happiness*. To outsiders, it seems to be set on easy mode. This game, however, is more treacherous. There are more sharks and stormier seas.

As the story begins, the sharks are obvious, with their pointed fins cutting slowly through the water. Later, they may be in various forms and wearing disguises. Beware!

A favorite author of mine is quoted, *all stories, if you follow them for long enough, end in tragedy. There's no true story teller who would tell you otherwise.*

That may be true.

Either way, time teaches us some simple lessons: drama imitates life, and stories repeat. In each, you can find three paradoxical characters who cyclically and inevitably experience a tragic ending.

The tragedy of drama itself: the persecutor, the rescuer, the victim. The tragedy of human-kind: individual liberties, human nature, an Earth with finite resources. The tragedy of the universe: time, ultimate purpose, human kind.

Lucky is a story, much like any other. It's fiction, nothing more; *folklore*[2], like the book's inspiration.

Some details are true, others aren't… but the details never were what was important. Stories are so much more than their details. The whole is greater than the sum of its parts.

Lucky is my story, our stories. Each of our stories are one in the same. A drop of rain becomes the sea. The story becomes the universe.

I am but a narrator, who discovered she can be the author and the illustrator of her own story. It turns out that we live in an incorporeal world in which you are what you believe.

There's so much information out there, you might say. *How can I know what to believe?*

Never in history has knowledge been so splintered, yet so accessible. Humankind has evolved in such a way that all our answers are literally a click away.

Life, then, is about asking the right questions.

Reality, it turns out, is not black and white. The paths society guides us down may not lead us down the road to happiness.

Paradoxically, all stories might *not* end in tragedy.

---

[2] Taylor Swift, *folklore*, Republic Records, 2020

Life can sometimes feel like you're swinging on an old rope swing with your hair flying in the wind as you bob back and forth between the *lakes of opposites*; of good and right and bad and wrong. But maybe, good, bad, right, and wrong are not ideas that should be analyzed amongst each other, rather, in accordance with a bigger picture.

Good and bad might not be opposites at all. Maybe the, seemingly dissonant, back and forth between these two forces can lead us towards finding our story's true purpose.

Over time, we take different roles in the different stories around us. Take note of how good can swiftly become evil. Power, wealth, success— hell, even love— have the power to corrupt. The key, then, to true happiness, may lie right around life's golden equilibrium; an area of transcendent, harmonious balance.

Lucky depicts two quintessential accounts of the *American Dream*, juxtaposed tales of glitter and tragedy. One is the story of an eccentric heiress[3], the other is the story of an international superstar[4]. Both depict a mercurial rise; then, the crater-sized wakes of destruction that seem to, inevitably, get left behind.

Their stories are but a backdrop to my discoveries. See, the pandemic changed me. Then, I needed to find myself again.

As I peered into the keyhole, I was led, as if on a celestial journey, through history, philosophy, mythology,

---

[3] Rebekah (Betty) West Harkness

[4] Rhea (Rae) Harmonía

music, math, and time. Trying to find order in the chaos, I studied the deep resonance of all the stories that came before me.

If you are curious enough, it seems, you can find answers in the depths of anything you are interested in.

Equipped with my new knowledge, I was able to re-write my own story in a way you never could imagine... but we'll save my story for another time. The story you're about to read is exciting enough.

2020 was a year of discovery for us all.

During its ups and downs, I drew a seemingly obvious conclusion: success and wealth aren't the fairy tales they are made out to be. Our world isn't what it is made out to be.

From my journey, this is what I give to you:

Reality is the ocean; our laws are the ship.
Many have never left the ship, jumped into the sea.
Jump in with me.

CHAPTER 1

TALE AS OLD AS TIME

"Trust in dreams, for in them is hidden the gate to eternity."
Khalil Gibran

It was a clear night. A gust of salty air drafted in the open window. The soothing crescendo of waves breaking against the boulders below kept the nanny, Miss Weeks, sound asleep. The Atlantic Ocean was lulling, over and over, *hush now, baby, hush.*

Miss Weeks slept soundly. She dreamt of melting clocks and a whimsical golden chalice that belonged to the queen of a fairy kingdom. The Chalice of Life.

In her dream, golden dust covered every surface. It twinkled down from a few pixies, who flitted about in the pink and purple tie-dyed sky above. On the chalice, jeweled butterflies clung to twisted, ascending golden roots.

The butterflies curled their wings, trying to fly, fly away; but found themselves firmly rooted.

A siren penetrated through the glistening air, causing the nanny to wake with a start. Angel was crying.

The nanny rose. She tiptoed down the thick carpet-padded hallway to the girl's room, taking care to step over the floor board that creaked.

It was a big, old house. The rest of the family was sleeping a few wings away, but as the woman started down the long hallway, she heeded caution. She took care never to disturb any spirits living in the walls.

Miss Weeks passed the large bay window. She stopped for a moment, taking in the view of the vast, dark Atlantic illuminated by the full moon. Then, she heard the girl scream out, again.

Screw the spirits; the nanny thought to herself, *they are awake now anyways.*

Angel's bedroom door was the second one on the left. When the woman got to it, she found that it was closed. Miss Weeks peered through the keyhole and saw thick, blonde hair cascading out from under the dust ruffle like a waterfall. The girl was hiding under the bed.

Angel was scared of many things— of haunted houses, of sharks, and of growing old. Her glistening eyes were windows to a tortured soul.

Miss Weeks pushed open the door and took a seat, cross legged, on the floor. "Bedtime story!" the girl pleaded, looking small, crumpled against the dust ruffle. Tears caught at her throat.

Angel delighted in stories of princesses and pirates, magic beans, and little elves who craft shoes.

Miss Weeks told the best stories.

The girl's doctor, however, had given the nanny a few restrictions: Angel could only be told some stories. The story must not upset her. The story must not help her confront the truth.

True stories can be scary.

True stories can make you think.

Miss Weeks mostly stuck to fairytales. She often took great creative liberties so that her stories would have happy endings. She never mentioned the wolves... Angel hadn't been ready for those stories just yet.

Wolves have sharp teeth and sly smiles. Wolves have been known to chew a person up and swallow them whole.

The situation around them, however, was growing increasingly fraught. Miss Weeks had talked to Angel's doctor this morning. They agreed, it may be time.

"Angel, I've been wanting to tell you a story about a girl that I used to know. Her memory has lingered in my mind across the years, as if the bold-inked headlines about her were tattooed onto my soul.

"Now, my dear, I don't want to give you the illusion that this is a happy story..."

Miss Weeks's words faded, as she recalled a conversation she had many years before. She encountered a man, Papa, who prophesied, *all stories, if continued far enough, end in loss; there is no true story teller who would keep that from you.*

Calamities have a tendency to come and then come again. Miss Weeks thought about Papa's words often.

"This story is a tragedy," the nanny continued, "and one of epic proportions. It is also, however, the story of overwhelming glitz and glamour; of a woman who cleaned her pool with Dom Pérignon and danced on tables until the wee hours of the morning with the legends of yesterday's tomorrow.

"It's the story of family; of tenacity, grit, and a tremendous amount of wealth. It's the story of love, but it's also the story of addiction. It's the story of greed and the story of loss.

"The story I am about to tell you, my dear, is the ultimate tale of the *American Dream*; it is the epitome of life, liberty, and the pursuit of happiness. It's a fairytale that every child, in even the dustiest corners of the universe, wishes they could write for themself.

"But Angel, it is also a cautionary tale. It's the story of how having everything makes a fairytale ending impossible."

Angel's blue eyes grew wide as Miss Weeks made her decision. It was time to open Pandora's box.

The nanny took a deep breath, then let it out slowly.

"This is the incredible story of the meteoric highs and devastating destruction, surrounding the life of Rebekah West Harkness.

"For most of her life, she went by the name, Betty."

"Time... now that's a truly curious thing. Looking back, it is interesting to think about which moments lead up to others.

Miss Weeks continued, "Some believe it's luck; others, destiny. Stories tend to repeat themselves. Time brings with it a sense of inevitability. Seconds, then centuries, tick away.

Stories are often told across generations, many times, before the greatest of them are ever written down. They are often told so lessons learned can withstand the test of time.

Of course, details may change any time a story is retold, abstracting it; but as is true with any tale, the objective reality was always impossible to see. The reality we experience is just the story our brain tells us. As the years pass, you'll find that you aren't your story's only illustrator.

Good stories can be found in many different forms, yet tend to conform to a similar structure. With a mindful eye and 20/20 vision, you may be able to identify the story's major elements— like the characters, setting, conflict, and resolution.

The plot of a good story, on the other hand, may be more abstract. The true message may be harder to pin down. The story may seem irrational or impossible. Good stories, though, are always about something important.

A story becomes a *good story* when it is told for a purpose.

But, Angel, the very best stories take it a step further. They draw you in. They make you feel something. They change who you are, at your very core.

These stories become the tattered books that are easiest to reach on your book case, littered with thin black lines, neon stripes, and scribbles in the margin. Every time you read it, you read a different story. Each time you read it, you learn something new about yourself. The greatest stories change alongside each new soul who experiences them.

Want to know something funny, Angel? Some of my favorite stories are tragedies.

Tragedies are stories that don't have happy endings. Tragedies employ drama; tragedies explore loss. Tragedies are more like life, my dear Angel. That's why I like them.

Life teaches the best lessons.

The problem with great stories is that they inevitably come to an end. At the end of a great tragedy, the reader comes to a humbling realization: the calamitous ending was not due to some error the characters made or something the characters did that the reader might have done differently. The end of the story could easily become the conclusion of yours.

Then the real tragedy hits... *the tragedy was inevitable.*

All of life is interconnected, Angel, like the branches of a five-hundred-year-old oak tree or the spidering web of veins and arteries in your lungs. We breathe in what plants breathe out, and they breathe in what we breathe out.

Rain falls from the heavens into the sea. Each drop becomes the ocean. Then it evaporates, and becomes the wispy pink and orange clouds you see on the horizon, right before the sun says goodnight. This is the circle of life.

It is easy, then, to see how stories are more than just stories. Stories are how we learn, how we remember, and how we experience. It may only be through stories that we can make sense of what is real, true, and possible.

You see, Angel, stories help us find patterns. They help us solve problems, find harmonies, and infer meaning. Stories create order in a chaotic world. Then, they make the chaos easier to cope with. Stories have the potential to provide identity and meaning to entire societies... and have done so for generations.

Nowadays, however, things have changed. We're ruled by different gods. Information is instant and limitless. Anyone has the power to write their own stories for all to hear. You can read anyone's story, and you don't even have to know how to read to do it. Pictures have taken the place of words. Possessions are the new symbols.

Some of this may be for the better... but how many of us wander through our daily realities with the lights off, miserably unaware that our stories are just that? A fish doesn't think about the ocean she swims in anymore than some of us take notice of the stories in which we exist. Many forget that reality is just our perception of it; others muddle through life without realizing the power their stories hold.

Story telling was once heralded as the key to making sense of a senseless world. Now, it no longer seems so important. Still, stories are constantly being constructed. They grow inside each of us, ready to be passed down to future generations. Some grow so big that the person bursts, and the story comes seeping out.

Folklore, sometimes sung around the campfire or whispered about at the neighborhood bar, is how mortals become legends. Stories are how we learn life's most important lessons and finally," Miss Weeks continued, smiling, "they are the best way for us to relish together in the curious, mystical, wondrous thing, I like to call the human experience."

CHAPTER 2

RHEA HARMONIA

"A dream you dream alone is only a dream.
A dream you dream together is reality."
John Lennon

I share a name with the mother of Zeus, a courageous goddess, born from the union of the Earth and the sky. Her name was Rhea.

Rhea means to flow, like the river.

On cold winter nights, Mom tucked me in under the flannel sheets. Safe, in my twin-sized bed, she told me tales of beautiful goddesses, fearless heroines, fairies, harpies, and monsters.

I'd fall asleep listening to those stories, then have vivid dreams of my own— of faraway times and mystical spaces.

Next to my bed, in a small, shadowy nook, housed a big, spiraled journal. Unlined.

My 'dream catcher.'

I rose with the sun... hoping to catch a dream in my net, not wanting to lose a single detail.

But a dream is not so easy to catch in the morning.

In my dream one night, I found myself in a vast, mystical forest, painted a deep evergreen. The sky was hazy orange, striped with fierce, fiery red streaks. I walked, not knowing where I was going but sensing that my journey would lead somewhere important.

I walked; then I walked some more.

Finally, I arrived upon a large clearing. A towering willow tree rooted herself in the middle, illuminated by the full moon. Her branches were dancing wildly in the wind.

I started dancing, too, twirling closer and closer to the tree. Something inside the tree's trunk was magnetic, exerting its forces onto my soul.

As I got closer, I started counting the branches trying to take in every detail. I counted hundreds before I got close enough to see that each branch spidered into thousands of other branches. Each branch had hundreds of long, thin leaves. They were shimmering and golden.

The branches and leaves twisted and tangled together as the wind blew, like they were dancing in the moonlight.

My own dance brought me closer to the tree's trunk. I examined the brown camouflage, where I came upon a small, wooden door. I rapped on it, thrice; it immediately swung open so wide, that I found myself inside a small room. I took in my surroundings.

An old lamp in the corner gave off a hazy glow. The walls were pitched in like a burlap tent and were the same color as the sky outside. In the corner, an old woman was rocking with her eyes closed. A spiral quilt was on her lap.

I sat next to the rocking chair, cross-legged, my eyes full of questions.

The old woman continued to rock; without opening her eyes, she began to speak. "This tree is my home. I call her zwń," she started, her voice a mere whisper. "She is the tree of life. Each branch, each leaf, is a story."

The woman took a sip from a small tea cup, "Would you like some, my dear?"

One, deep gong resonated from an old grandfather clock in the back of the room. Suddenly, a tea cup appeared in front of me filled with a murky liquid. I took a tentative sip.

Ahhh, Chamomile.

When I looked back down at my cup, a glistening, golden fog hid the dark tea inside. I peered up at the old woman in the rocking chair. I watched her closely, confused. She blew on her tea cup. I did the same.

I watched the fog in my cup disappear revealing a golden, infinite lotus. Each petal depicted a different story. Some stories I knew well. Others, I didn't recognize.

The lotus revealed story after story until finally the old woman broke her silence. "When a tree's roots are well-nourished and rain falls often," she said, "the tree will grow tall. A termite infection at one level could cause massive damage to the other branches. It could destroy the entire ecosystem."

I looked at the old woman, stunned. "The tree may die? Where would you live then?" The old woman replied, "It may die. It may not."

She was silent for a long moment before she whispered, "I can always plant another."

When Mom was pregnant with me, she played a Bach record while she folded laundry and sang me lullabies at night. She and Dad drove to their first sonogram with *Blonde in the Bleachers* blasting from the speakers of my mom's cherry red '85 Ford Escort.

That was the day they heard my heartbeat for the first time. Inside Mom's womb, the rhythm of my life was the steady beat of her heart. When I kicked my legs, the beat got stronger. Music was the first story I ever heard.

Our life is like music, you know. Rhythmical, irrational. A story.

Inside a story, I lose track of time; lost, on journeys to places I'll never go and lifetimes I'll never experience. A good story is like a good song; a mystical, beautiful representation of life.

I remember Mom telling me, "Be careful of the stories you tell, and be wary of the stories you're told." I was too young to understand, but she giggled and whispered anyways: "I have a secret for you, Baby. Stories are all we are."

Stories are all we are, thus, one must be careful. Stories are powerful. Some are dangerous; others help us find our truth. Some stories help us forget that 'the collective truth' may not be true at all. Other stories teach us that the ultimate truth is only found within.

If you want to know the real truth, you've got to spend enough time with it. That's why I started writing this book.

There was a point in my life when I thought I had the world figured out. I had money; I had power. I thought I could control the narrative. I thought I could master the universe.

Then, I came to a sobering realization. I had storied my life all wrong.

My life had turned into something I couldn't control. I was lost in the chaos, overwhelmed by the randomness.

Then, I heard a story about a butterfly.

Dad's friend, Ed, was a weatherman on channel 9's evening news. One night, at dinner, Ed told him, "A butterfly over in China almost lost me my job!"

Apparently, this butterfly had, quite literally, flapped her wings at the wrong place at the wrong time and caused an unforeseen hurricane over New York Harbor and the Rhode Island Coast. Many of the little New England coastal towns were wiped out, almost completely.

Homes destroyed. Eight died.

Ed was to blame.

But, by tracking this butterfly, Ed found that a slight variation in starting parameters rendered his entire weather prediction model to descend into chaos. Ed told Dad, "Unless I was there at the exact moment the hurricane started, and had perfectly precise measurements… well, there was no way to have predicted it!"

Ed went home and thought about it.

Then, he realized: *the more data run through a system, the more accurate the prediction*. Ed decided to switch his weather prediction model to a system that placed more weight on historical averages and found far more accuracy.

Other meteorologists followed suit. Historical averages are how most predict the weather today.

You may see why it is important then— if we're to sort through the chaos— to go back to the very beginning. We must go back before fairy tales, before stories were written down.

We must go back to when a *story* was but a *myth*.

My freshman lit teacher, Mr. Hillman, was a mythological thinker ahead of his time. He attempted an epic feat… to teach a bunch of 15-year olds to unlock the dimensions of universal mystery.

The key? "Books!" he lectured.

What he really meant was the story inside the book. The archetype that all stories are based on.

Scribbled in the margins of my English notebook was this:

Without myth, you take life as it is presented to you. You take life literally and not mythically. You take life as fact rather than something that has to do with imagination.

Ancient Greek myths are widely-thought to be the beginning of all stories. They are the tales of our lives and others. They are the beginning of each work of art and each piece of music, each pact of love and each act of war.

Myths help us connect to each other, to understand each other. They relay lessons and warnings. They paint dreams of what the future may hold. They allow us to story and learn upon the past.

Myths are the heartbeat of every human on the planet no matter how far apart they are in distance or time, in fantasy or reality. Some say, myths give children heroes and the template from which they grow and develop. But more importantly, stories teach children how to use their imagination. Stories teach us about hope.

Stories remind us how valuable and intrinsically meaningful our lives really are, even at times when they don't feel they are. They show us patterns in the chaos. Stories have the power to save us.

Stories saved me.

One of my favorite stories is set sometime close to the beginning.

According to legend, Eternity was torn between passion and time, eternal and opposing forces. He birthed Rhea and Kronos, who were complete opposites. Their tension was a perfect storm; they were drawn to each other as if they, too, were made to recreate. When they danced, their cyclic alternation created Earth and time as we know it.

Fresh from their dance, beside himself in ecstasy, Kronos picked Eternity up and swallowed him whole. Rhea was devastated. To make amends, Kronos gave Rhea the Earth.

Through their dance, Rhea and Kronos birthed five gods, each more powerful than the last. Finally, Rhea bore Zeus, the most powerful of them all.

One dark night, before their first baby was born, Kronos dreamt of a pregnant Rhea, illuminated, in the starry sky. She told him, "Kronos, I have read your fate. One day, you, too, will be defeated by your own child."

When Kronos woke, he was literally blinded by his own fury. He banished the pregnant Rhea to Earth and told her that when the child is born, she must return to him with the baby.

On Earth, all alone, Rhea wept.

Her tears filled entire lakes and oceans. Her anguish turned the wind into dust.

Finally, her child was born.

When she returned to Kronos, he was waiting for her upon the highest peak of Mount Olympus.

"Give me the child," Kronos roared.

Rhea handed him the infant and turned away, not able to bear the sight of Kronos doing the inevitable.

She wept and she wept.

Kronos dried her tears and asked her to dance.

Then, the cycle repeated again, and again, and again, and again. Rhea was locked in a wheel of tragedy.

Dance, hope, sorrow. Dance, hope, sorrow.

When she delivered her fifth child, Poseidon, Rhea mustered the courage to watch as Kronos swallowed him whole. Horrified, Rhea pledged not to let the tragedy repeat itself, once again. She beckoned the birds to claw out Kronos's ears, rendering him deaf.

Still, she wept. Still, Kronos dried her tears. Still, they danced.

However, when Zeus was born, Rhea did not deliver him to Mount Olympus. Instead, hoping to outwit Kronos, she brought him a stone.

Blind and deaf, Kronos took the stone and swallowed it without thinking twice. He then rested easy, content, thinking all of his children were safe and controlled inside his belly.

Zeus, however, was not safe inside of Kronos; he was hidden in a small cave in the mountains of Crete. Before she delivered the stone, Rhea tucked the child away to be raised by a nymph. She left him with just the story of his siblings. When Zeus was 21-years-old, Rhea visited him in Crete to remind him of his power and responsibility.

Wrecked with a tension of guilt and hubris, Zeus trained hard. He became powerful enough to face his father in battle to avenge his mother and rescue his siblings.

He snuck up to Mount Olympus alongside his abiding mother. When Kronos was distracted, Zeus took a thunderbolt and sliced his father's body from his heart to his belly button, freeing his siblings. As they went off, to rule various Earthly entities, like the underworld and the sea, Zeus stitched his father up and banished him to a far-off land.

A few moments later, the newly crowned Zeus sat on his throne on Mount Olympus. He admired the foamy sea, as Aphrodite emerged— shimmering, lovely, and golden. With incomparable beauty and unmatched charm, Aphrodite enchanted gods and mortals alike. Anywhere she went, a flock of white doves followed, searching for the pleasure, beauty, and passion promised.

Aphrodite's personality, however, did not match her bewitching features. She was unable to pass a body of water without stopping to gaze at her reflection. She was ill-tempered and easily offended.

It wasn't just that the love goddess was vain, though, despite the rumors. Those who knew Aphrodite, knew this: she never felt quite sure of herself. She had an insatiable and puzzling need to prove to the world how beautiful and valuable she really was.

Zeus, who adopted Aphrodite when she rose from the sea, became increasingly wary of his daughter. It was clear to him that she had no control of her desires— Aphrodite broke up marriages and drove gods to madness.

I need to find a perfect match for Aphrodite, Zeus thought; *her eternal soulmate.*

Heph was an ideal pick. First of all, Zeus owed him a favor. Heph built all the palaces for the gods on Mount Olympus. Second, Heph's passion for fire matched that of Aphrodite's for love. Third, he was ugly as sin.

Tension of opposites, thought Zeus, *makes for a match made in heaven.*

The next Tuesday, as the sun set upon Mount Olympus, *Pomp and Circumstance* played. Aphrodite walked somberly down the aisle towards Heph, who gawked at her. Her in white; him in his finest purple robe. He looked up at her and grinned like the devil.

There was little harmony in their marriage. It was soon clear, to all of the gods, that Heph and Aphrodite were no perfect pair. He strayed to others. So did she.

As if pulled together like beads on a golden string, Aphrodite began an affair with her childhood lover. His name was Ares.

Ares was the god of war.

Ares's passion for war truly matched Aphrodite's for love; their affair felt far more like fate.

Aphrodite would sneak Ares into bed each day when the sun was highest in the sky. They made passionate love while Heph was busy working in his blacksmith shop playing with fire.

One day, Heph came home early because he was sick. He walked in the door and saw clothes strewn about. Upstairs, the lovers— his wife and his friend— were lost in a passionate embrace in Heph's own bed.

Heph was furious.

Heph stayed up late that night plotting his revenge. He crafted a golden web to trap his wife and her lover in their adulterous act. The next day, he sent a scroll to the other gods via messenger pigeon.

My house, when the sun is at its highest.

-H

At noon, the gods gathered for Heph's scheme on the highest peak of Mount Olympus. Heph made sure Aphrodite and Ares were in bed together, naked, before he activated his trap.

Finally, Heph exposed the lovers.

Thunderous laughter rang out from the clouds above, as Aphrodite and Ares's faithless embrace was displayed for all to see. Embarrassed, Aphrodite reached her hand around, searching for something to cover her naked, reddening body.

Poor, vain Aphrodite thought all the gods were laughing at her.

Heph was closer to the laughing gods, however, and could hear their jabber.

"I wouldn't kick Aphrodite out of my bed," Nike, the god of victory bellowed. "Who could blame her?! If I was married to that ogre, Heph, I'd have an affair too!"

Zeus thundered from on high and banished Ares to Earth to slither around for eternity. Aphrodite wept and wept. Ares was her one true love.

Later that night, a haunting secret spilled out of the distraught Aphrodite. She was pregnant. Ares was the father. The baby would be a girl.

Even more enraged, humiliated, Heph banished the pregnant goddess from his home. Aphrodite had nowhere to turn but to her father's house. She knocked on the door of Zeus and when he answered, she was on her knees.

"Please forgive me, Father," she wept, "but my heart loves another. I cannot stay with Heph any longer. I cannot stay upon Mount Olympus any longer. I must be on Earth with my love."

Zeus nodded, forlorn. He finally understood.

Love and war: the ultimate *tension of opposites*.

He made an agreement with his adopted daughter.

"Aphrodite, you will stay on Mount Olympus until your child is born; then, you will be allowed to go to Earth to be with your love," the god boomed.

Zeus had one caveat, however. The baby would be left behind for him to raise as his own. Aphrodite reluctantly agreed.

Finally, the baby came. Just as the mama had foreseen, Aphrodite's child was a beautiful and healthy baby girl. She was named Harmonía.

Then, Aphrodite was sent to Earth, in the form of a serpent, to spend eternity slithering around with her star-crossed lover. According to legend, Aphrodite and Ares lived happily ever after.

Now, you may be wondering... what ever happened to that stolen child of love and war— the beautiful Harmonía? Well, we'll save her story for later. Stay tuned; it's a good one.

I think it might be time to introduce myself.

My name is Rhea Harmonía.

Most people call me Rae, like the sun.

All I've ever wanted to do is make music.

The story of my life begins in a snow globe, on a little Christmas tree farm, in small-town Pennsylvania. A tiny Rae, her frizzy golden curls circling her head like Athena's crown, sits on a couch in her family's living room, surrounded by the people who love her most. The girl's small fingers strum the strings of a guitar. Outside, a fresh blanket of snow has turned the world white.

I travel back in time. Pennsylvania's clear, night sky guides me. The twinkling stars of the universe shine in my mind's eye. I can smell pine needles and butterscotch from the fresh evergreen tree in the corner. I feel the soft cotton of Gram's hand-stitched, spiral quilt on my lap. I feel the waxy surface of my very own guitar, a birthday gift. I feel throbbing in my fingers which become more and more mutilated with each strum.

My little fairytale world was so safe.

My family just finished putting the ornaments on the tree. Dad plugged in the string of Christmas lights wrapped around the tree. Mom turned off the lamp. The three of us sat on the sofa and admired our hard work.

Each ornament was like a planet; an illuminated juxtaposition against a starry, evergreen sky. Each one is special. Each has a story.

Mom pulled a string. "Let there be light," she proclaimed!

I wanted to be the one to put the star on the top of the tree, but I was too small. My dad swung me upon his shoulders, like I was weightless, helping me grow.

Seven feet in the sky, and finally, I could reach the tallest branch. I placed the star on top.

Like those who came before me, I had the purest intentions.

CHAPTER 3

THE CONFEDERATE SOLDIER

"Unless we learn from history, we are destined to repeat it. This is no longer merely an academic exercise, but may contain our world's fate and our destiny."
Alex Haley

Miss Weeks cleared her throat.

She continued, "The story of Betty West Harkness begins in a young America with her hard-working and tenacious grandfather, Thomas West.

Thomas grew up on a small plantation in sunny South Carolina. Each day passed alongside nature's clock. He and his three brothers woke before sunrise and worked the fields until the sun went down. The farmhands, who his father had purchased a few years prior, joined them.

Though Thomas's father owned just a few slaves, the West family treated them well. The men and the slaves worked together in the fields and ate from the same pot at dinner. Thomas's father was known to say, *I should treat em' right; I want to get the most interest out of my investment.*

Almost everything that Thomas or his siblings needed, his mother and father manufactured themselves at the plantation. Their entrepreneurial spirit embodied everything that the *American Dream* was supposed to attract.

His mother spun wool from cotton to sew clothes. She then dyed them; the blues came from wild Indigo in the woods and darker colors made from walnut juice, copperas, and ground herbs.

Thomas's father grew, slaughtered, and preserved his own livestock. The family ate the stock of meat throughout the year. Wheat, rice, vegetables, potatoes, milk, eggs, and butter were all produced on the farm. His mother broiled sea water for salt and his father learned to extract sugar from sugar cane. The family nor their slaves ever went hungry.

Many of their neighbors had recently packed their belongings into big covered wagons to begin the journey west in search of glittering riches. Thomas was devastated when the family next door packed their wagon. Their son, Peter, was his best friend in the whole wide world.

A few months later, Thomas got a letter from the boy with detailed instructions of how to find him out west. Peter carved star formations in rocks along the way so that Thomas could easily follow their trail.

The West family didn't need to travel west, however. They had a gold mine right in their own backyard.

The Wests had been lucky enough to come to America at a time when it paid to be white. The cotton industry made it easy for Thomas's father, along with many other immigrants, to take advantage of a society that allowed people to get rich quick.

In this day and age, slave labor reigned supreme. Enslaved black men were the most valuable equities one could own. Cotton had quickly become America's most valuable export. America, where many of the world's most innovative entrepreneurs came in quest of a better life, had plenty of farmable land. Cotton farms popped up everywhere.

In the South, labor costs were low due to high supply. Businesses began to compete over the price, not the quality, of their goods.

My dear Angel, stories like this one are a breeding ground for inequality and poverty.

Thomas's father had also come to this sobering realization. The economy around him was growing at an astonishing pace. If he was unable to grow at a similar pace, his family's prosperity would die.

Thomas and his father joined the local chapter of a secret farm fraternity. Each month, the farmers gathered to discuss the economic and agricultural well-being of the community they ruled.

In a hazy room, filled with smoking pipes and dwindling whiskey, the men were conflicted. Many had come to the same realization as Thomas's father. Business was cut throat. In this capitalist world you had to eat, or you'd be eaten. You had to take or you'd be taken from.

Some found that it was far easier to incentivize their workers, especially the slaves, through punishment instead of promotion.

Farmers associations across the South were having similar discussions. *Grow or die. Punishment works better than promotion.*

Slaves began to grow and pick cotton at a backbreaking speed. The country's supply of cotton increased exponentially. Farmers and their investors rejoiced. Money came easily.

It was a flush time of fever dreams; the South capitalized on the scarred backs of the enslaved as the railroad tracks of American industrialization were being laid. The combination was like lighting a stick of dynamite. Our young country was on the cusp of an economic boom. Through his father, Thomas learned lessons that would help him build a vast fortune.

The South was abusing their workers, though, my dear Angel. This became especially clear to the rest of the nation when it began to have a direct impact on the U.S. economy. The South's dogma of *punishment over promotion* quickly led to an overproduced cotton supply.

With an abundance of cotton, the value of cotton dissipated. The market value of the labor force fell in a similar manner; slaves that were being bought for over $2000 a year prior, now sold on the auction block for just $75.

Thomas's father owed the bank three times as much as the family made in revenue that year, and many other farmers were in the same boat. Cotton was their cash cow. Slaves were their 401K.

Banks found themselves in a sticky situation. They had written loans to any white man who could sign his name. Now, those men were unable to pay what they owed. The banks' investors, including state governments, were delighted to see an increase of loans being written, but were now outraged that the banks couldn't make interest payments on their bonds.

The banks knew, however, if they simply foreclosed on the farmers unable to make payments on their loans, those customers would simply leave.... and take their slaves and any residual value out of America and over to Texas.

It was a lose-lose situation. The American economy was crumbling. The federal government had to step in and do something.

Cotton slavery had gotten too big to fail.

After the Panic of 1837, Thomas's family was never the same. One winter, his father decided that they needed new machinery to keep up with the other farms in their town.

That year, Thomas's mother didn't get a single Christmas present. Thomas and his brothers each got a marble in their stockings.

As Thomas grew up, he yearned for a life worth more. He started sweet-talking the pretty little neighbor girl named Florence.

I think I am going to marry her someday, the young boy thought to himself, as visions of their future danced in his head. Thomas pictured him and Florence walking down the aisle. He saw her belly get bigger. He imagined their first child.

If he closed his eyes tightly, he could see their family in a little salt-box house on the coast. He imagined their kids playing in the sand, laughing and smiling, building castles, and collecting sand dollars. Everyone was so happy.

Thomas worked day in and day out in the fields. He read books. Each night, he got on his knees and prayed for an opportunity to make something of his life. When that opportunity came, he would know for certain that his life had true meaning.

As he slept, the Civil War dawned.

General Nathan Bedford Forrest traveled to South Carolina, and his troop of Confederate soldiers marched up and down the streets of Thomas's town, tacking a crisply printed recruitment pamphlet on each door. Thomas, blinded by patriotic zeal and quest for opportunity, succumbed to General Forrest's ideals of heroics and legacy.

He enlisted.

As he marched out the front door in a gray wool uniform with shiny buttons, Florence, the pretty neighbor girl, bid him goodbye with her handkerchief waving.

Thomas was off to fight the Union.

The war was nothing like Thomas had anticipated. His threadbare uniform barely kept him warm despite the mild Southern winters. His left boot had a hole near the big toe, and he left a faint trail of blood in the snow as the troops marched north, single file.

Lice, malaria, and tuberculosis ran rampant throughout the troops. Fresh meat and coffee rations became incredibly scarce, and Thomas quickly became under nourished. His battalion foraged in the forest for fresh vegetables and pillaged whatever they could from farms along their route.

Word of their thievery spread through the battleground. General Forrest was increasingly worried that, sooner or later, a disgruntled farm owner would try to poison the entire group.

General Forrest, who later went on to be elected as the first Grand Wizard of the Ku Klux Klan, had a striking, yet commanding presence. On the battleground, everyone was terrified of the General and for good reason.

He knew that the key to getting ahead in life could only be found outside of the rule book.

Thomas liked him, though. He respected his logic and rationality. See, Angel, General Forrest knew that reality was largely about perception.

At one battle in Alabama, Thomas and his fellow soldiers were led up a cliff, down the cliff, and back up again. They repeated this many times. The Union cavalry, thinking that Thomas's troop had three times as many men, surrendered immediately.

Thomas was thankful no blood was shed that day.

Thomas left for the war an innocent boy and returned a disturbed man. The horrors of his wartime experiences haunted him. At night, he struggled to fall asleep. When he finally managed to soothe himself into a slumber, Thomas experienced a recurring nightmare.

In it, Thomas was running across the rugged Tennessee terrain. Behind him, two hundred black Union soldiers were chasing him, guns drawn. He ran and ran, as fast as he could.

He was never fast enough, though, and had to hide. Behind a bush, he slowed his breath, careful not to make any sudden movements. But then, inevitably, he was found.

The whites of Thomas's eyes met with another soldier's yellowing sclera. He then looked down and saw a black finger pulling back the trigger of a long, shiny rifle.

Crack!

At this point in the dream, Thomas woke, with a start.

Each night, Thomas made it slightly further away from the battleground at which his battalion had claimed victory. But the black soldiers would always get him... just like Thomas got them.

Clammy and sweaty, Thomas had to swallow back a coppery wave of nausea as he tried not to disturb Florence who was laying next to him.

He never talked about it, Angel; not with his sons or his wife. Nobody knew what really happened in the war. Nobody knew the horrors of what Thomas and his troops really did.

Thomas used the few dollars he saved during the war to buy the neighbor girl, Florence, a ring. With his army pension as a safety net, they moved their growing family to a land of potential and opportunity. Thomas was finally following the neighbor boy west.

Out west, Thomas's life would be worth more.

St. Louis, Missouri was the fourth largest city in the nation: second only to Chicago in terms of railroad crossings. Thomas passed the time on the train to Missouri dreaming about the World's Fair, the upcoming Olympic Games, and reading Horatio Alger's *Do and Dare*. Florence embroidered daisies on a baby blanket for the little human forming itself in her belly. She had a hunch that it was going to be a girl.

On the train, Florence told Thomas stories of her older brother, Brian, who had recently made Cleveland home.

Brian bought himself a ticket to New York City the day he turned eighteen. He identified a golden opportunity in a growing sector of the economy— finance. Brian was employed in various positions in New York's Financial District and he enjoyed the work.

When Brian's friend came to him with a business opportunity in Cleveland, he seized it. Cleveland was a growing, prosperous new city. It was ripe with opportunity, especially in finance. Brian quickly found a way to utilize his expertise to take advantage of the growing economy. He established a trust company and managed the investments of his friends and their families.

Thomas and Florence's journey would take them through Cleveland. Brian invited the couple to stay with him for a few days. Thomas used the opportunity to learn the method behind Brian's madness.

A few days later, jostling around next to Florence en route to their final destination, Thomas sketched out his plans towards realizing the *American Dream*. In St. Louis, very much like Cleveland, there was opportunity for anyone to make something of themselves... as long as they were willing to put in a lot of hard work.

Thomas started by using the little extra money he earned from his pension each month to buy livestock which he then bred and sold on the up. He opened a little two-lane, duckpin bowling alley. Florence sold snacks, drinks, and convenience items to their customers. They opened an inn.

There was no federal income tax at this time and Thomas, Betty's grandfather, was making more money than he knew what to do with. Flush with cash, he invested his money in an idea he had sketched out, on the train, a few years earlier. A bank.

It was a slam dunk investment decision. Immediately successful, Thomas's bank had almost more customers than he could handle.

One day, a friend passed through whom Thomas fought with during the war. His friend had gone onto Washington after the war and gotten involved in politics.

This friend told Thomas that one day, very soon, the government would be passing a $2.00 per gallon tax on whiskey. Proportionally massive, this tax came at a time when a shot of spirits would only set you back about $0.04.

Thomas saw the opportunity with a glint in his eye. He said, to himself, *there's money to be made here.*

Thomas invested every single dollar in his bank and became the largest distributor of whiskey in St. Louis, a decision that netted him close to $2 million in today's money.

This was not without risk, of course... or damage.

Thomas's customer's cash was all tied up, due to his speculation. Sometimes, Thomas had to resort to drastic measures to keep his boat from overflowing.

Once, trying to stall an angry farmer looking for his money, Thomas had his secretary sing Christmas carols in the front lobby for fifteen minutes, while Thomas ran to the corner store to borrow the $89 in cash that he needed.

The media was on to Thomas's antics; one headline screamed!

Thomas West: Robin Hood or Robber Baron?

Still, Thomas's risk-garnered reward provided him with ample means to invest in another idea inspired by his brother-in-law.

Brian found massive success with his Cleveland Trust Company. He often wrote Thomas to tell him of his good fortunes. Then, one snowy Christmas eve, the two men realized that there wasn't a single trust company west of Cleveland.

So, Thomas set out to establish one in St. Louis, and he very successfully did just that.

The St. Louis Trust Company catapulted the West family into a position of status in a cruel order of social hierarchy, in a booming city at the brink of the Industrial Revolution."

Miss Weeks paused to catch her breath. Angel continued to stare at her, transfixed.

CHAPTER 4

PURE INTENTIONS

"The evil that is in the world almost always comes of ignorance, and good intentions may do as much harm as malevolence if they lack understanding."
Albert Camus

I think of my childhood and see an enchanted dreamscape: a tiny Rhea Harmonía, running free in the forest and riding horses. When I was a kid, my parents let my imagination run wild. No surface was off limits for art. Still, they kept me rational.

"Be logical, Rae," Dad implored.

Dad was acutely aware that I was born into the world of business: where my value as a person would be largely defined by how much financial value I created for the world.

That's why they started calling me Rae. Rae is an androgynous name; a name that didn't immediately identify me as a woman when read from a business card or at the top of a resume. My dad envisioned my future as a climb up the corporate ladder... maybe to a cushy corner-office job.

He didn't want me to be discriminated against for being a woman.

My life was a dream; so, of course, it was sometimes hard to fall asleep. Mom soothed me to sleep with stories. Some were from her imagination, but she'd often turn to an old friend, like Emily Dickinson.

One night, I woke with a start, a rhyme stuck in my head:

I'm Nobody! Who are you?
Are you – Nobody – too?
Look, there's a pair of us!

Words fascinate me. I've always enjoyed putting them together in different patterns to tell stories. Words are puzzle pieces I can arrange in such a way to change the world around me.

As I grew, my vocabulary grew with me. As my vocabulary grew, so did my world.

I experienced more good times and more bad. Mom and I went to a LeAnn Rimes concert. I giggled, danced in my chair, and sang along. Life was great; I was happy! I did something naughty, and Dad banished me to my room. Life was horrible; I was sad!

In 'time out,' I closed my eyes and dreamt up a poem. Weaving words together was soothing; creating poems made me feel happy. Then, I recited the poem for my brother, and he teased me. I felt sad again.

As my world grew, so did my perception of life's experiences. The highs felt higher and the lows felt lower.

One warm August morning, Mom tied a bow in my hair; Dad grabbed my backpack from the hook next to the door. They walked me down the driveway where a big yellow school bus was waiting to pick me up.

Dad said, "I like your plaid dress, Baby." It was my new school uniform.

Mom asked the bus driver his name.

"Larry," the chubby bald man said; "I promise I will get your daughter to and from school safely, Ma'am. It's my purpose in life!"

Dad kissed me on my forehead. Mom hugged me extra tight. She pulled me close and whispered, "Rhea, there's a light inside of you that shines brighter than the lights in New York City. Don't let the world dull your sparkle."

Sitting on the cracked pleather bus seat, my backpack beside me, I closed my eyes and imagined the city. I saw twinkling lights. Someday, I would get out of Pennsylvania and see the bright city lights for myself.

Larry kept his promise for many years. Bright and early, he'd arrive at the end of my long driveway. He sat, in his big yellow school bus, waiting for me. A few years later, my brother joined us.

"Good morning, Rhea," he said as I got on the bus. "Have a nice day at school, Rhea," as he dropped me off.

Some days were better than others. Then, like clockwork, 3 o'clock would roll around, and Larry was there waiting in his big yellow school bus.

"How was your day, Rhea?"

Then, "Enjoy your evening, Rhea."

Larry was always so nice to me. He cared about all of the kids on the bus.

My classmates, however, were not always so kind...

One day, Sam hollered, "Josh, don't you think Rhea looks like a Golden Retriever?" Josh thought that was hilarious, of course, so he told everyone in the class. Suddenly, instead of answering me when I asked a question, my classmates only barked.

That episode lasted a few weeks.

On the playground, Morgan tripped me. Ms. Scott, the recess aide, said it was an accident, but I saw the glint in Morgan's eye before she did it.

Blood dripped down my knee. My dignity was stained with mud. The nurse let me cry in her office for thirty minutes before sending me back to class.

The bright, city light inside me dimmed each time someone was mean. Sometimes the world felt so dark. I wasn't good enough. I didn't fit in. All I wanted was for people to like me, to belong.

This was my life, though.

Larry picked me up. The kids at school were mean. Larry dropped me off at the end of my long driveway.

Mom would be standing there, waiting for me, always. I'd cry to her, quite literally on her shoulder, for no more than fifteen minutes. I, then, retreated to my room.

Safe behind a locked door, I might cry some more, read, write poems, or pray for the weekend.

The weekends came, then went, too quickly. In the fall, sometimes Mom took me horseback riding. In the summer, sometimes Dad took my brother and me to the amusement park. But Monday always came around again.

"Time for school, Rae!"

Larry picked me up. Kids were mean. Larry dropped me off. I cried to Mom, then sulked in my room.

This was my life.

Lather, rinse, repeat.

I was so excited to start middle school. In middle school, I would have a locker and eight different classes during the day. In middle school, the kids were older and more mature. In middle school, more people would like me.

Mom agreed... this would be my year!

At first, it was.

I sat next to a popular girl, Jennifer, in math class. We compared schedules.

"Yes! We both have 4th period lunch!"

Jennifer invited me to sit with her friends at the lunch table. I told one of the girls, Paige, that I liked her headband. Morgan and I giggled about the cute boy who sat next to me in class. The girls and I talked about music. I told them about my favorites— James Taylor, LeAnn Rimes, and of course, Lizzie and Kevin Starr.

Lunch, for a while, was heaven... but it quickly became my personal hell.

One day, Nicole taunted, "Rhea has the frizziest hair in school." A few days later, Morgan made up a code name for me. At the lunch table, the girls talked shit about me in front of me. It wasn't long before the popular girls ghosted me. Apparently, Jennifer told them, "Let's just pretend Rhea isn't there."

Paige still talked to me outside of lunch. At the table, though, it was like I didn't exist.

I was too young. I didn't grasp the severity of what was happening. Still, I heard Mom's words in my ear. A warning: *stories are all we are, Baby.*

These girls had knocked me down to the role of victim in the main story of my life.

Mom dried my tears and told me, "In life, you never want to cast yourself as the role of the victim. Not all of the characters make it out of the story alive."

Mom taught me how to identify the villain, the hero, and the victim in any story. The villain is the persecutor, who bulldozes anyone who may get in their way. The hero is the rescuer, who swoops in to save the day. The victim is the one who always needs saving.

Driven further away from my truth, I didn't know if I would make it out of this story alive. I did know one thing, however: victimhood was not my story.

The next day, I switched lunch tables.

It was a good lesson to begin to learn young... if you can't control what role others take in your story, then you are the one who needs to change.

I tried out for soccer but didn't make the team. It seems that I lack a certain crucial skill set for sport— hand eye coordination. I focused on what I was good at: English homework, singing in the shower, playing the guitar, and writing.

I tried out for *Hello, Dolly* with a local musical theatre troupe. To my surprise, I got a lead role. "Oh dear, oh my!" I trilled from the stage, my voice projecting, without a microphone towards the back corners of the theatre. "Would you look at that! The shop isn't open yet?!"

On the last day of the show, at curtain call, the director gave out a few awards. "Finally, the award for *Brightest Sparkle*, goes to Rae Harmonía," he paused, "for never losing character, even when she was in the background." I felt my chest inflate.

Life at school, however, never got much easier.

I couldn't understand why people were so mean to me. I was nice to everyone; I stuck up for people who were being bullied. I baked chocolate-chip cookies for my entire class.

When I got older, I read self-help books. My favorite? *How to Win Friends and Influence People.* I followed all of Dale's rules. I smiled at everyone, I greeted them by name. I asked questions, I honed my listening skills.

Nothing was ever enough.

Safe inside my twin sized bed, I cried. "My life is a tragedy!"

Mom sat next to me and stroked my curls. She re-told me the story of Harmonía and reminded me of how Harmonía became her own hero. Mom stressed, "Never accept the role of victim in your own story."

The darkness I was surrounded by at school had caused me to turn inward. I lacked the fundamental sense of belonging that I needed to live life like all of my peers. I dove deeper into writing; words became my way of filtering the world.

I started writing songs. I wrote dozens.

I played Mom one of my songs, and her face transformed into something that I had never seen before: a mixture of happiness, surprise, and pride. It made me feel sparkly.

Pretty soon, that sparkly feeling sparked more often.

When I played someone a song, their face became transfixed, like Mom's. This made me feel valuable. It made me feel like I was doing something good.

Sure, my classmates didn't like me, but who needed them anyways?

My family hosted performances. They were small; my dad's 40th birthday, happy hour at the local coffee shop, then at the neighborhood park. Mom and I passed out flyers at the park a few days beforehand, and over a hundred people showed up. It was my biggest concert yet.

On an unseasonably warm weekend in March, Mom and I made the 10-hour drive to Nashville. A few months earlier, at a karaoke night with the *Hello, Dolly* cast, the director suggested to Mom that I focus my attention on country music.

He told her, "Rae has potential, Mrs. Harmonía. Real potential."

Potential. I liked that word.

After that, the Harmonía family made country music the soundtrack of our home. I wrote dozens of songs and practiced singing with a Southern twang. I studied YouTube videos of country stars. Then my brother filmed me with Dad's tape recorder.

I watched back my own videos, over and over. Static played as I rewound the tape to watch it again: me in costume, singing with a Southern twang, and strumming my guitar.

I couldn't wait to get to Nashville.

Nashville was my dream. Nashville was country music heaven.

Our trip marked my first time in Tennessee. Mom and I walked down Broadway and marveled at the big signs and neon lights. Then, we toured the Johnny Cash museum. Mom loves Johnny Cash. She always says, "He's my muse."

After the museum, Mom drove me to each and every record label on Music Row. Like clockwork, I got out of the Denali, smoothed my sundress, and clicked my cowboy boots. Mom handed me a bag that held my demo tape, a glamour shot, and our contact information.

I ran into the studio and introduced myself to the young, always blonde secretary sitting in front. I'd ask, sweetly, "Is *(insert CEO's name here)* in?" But, of course, he was never available. So, I would leave my goodie bag with the receptionist, who always promised to pass it on.

On the way back to Pennsylvania, I called my brother on Mom's flip phone. "I think it went well," I gushed. "I am going to get a record deal. I just know it!"

When we got back to Pennsylvania, though, life drudged on. My phone didn't ring.

I hand-delivered my music to every record label on Music Row. Not a single one of them called me back.

My goal had been set, though. I was going to get a record deal. Music was my story.

I can't give up, I just need to figure out what to do next.

The epiphany came while sitting in the stands of my brother's little league baseball game. "You know what would be a great way to sing in front of a bunch of people?" I asked

Mom. I followed up with, "Singing the national anthem… I could probably get in front of thousands of people this way!"

I sent dozens of demo tapes across the state of me singing the National Anthem. I knew I needed to get my face out there in order to make my dream come true.

Calls started flowing in, responding to the tapes.

I sang the National Anthem anywhere I possibly could: garden clubs, middle school graduations, and the local Little League baseball championship. One night, I even got a call to sing at a 76ers game!

I didn't care where I sang, though. I just wanted to do it in front of a crowd.

My life had become all about music.

Write, sing, listen. *Lather, rinse, repeat.*

Music was like a lighthouse, shining bright and strong, guiding me out of the dark abyss I had fallen into. Music made me feel like I was good enough. Singing for people and sharing my stories helped me feel valuable. When I performed, I was being the best Rae I could be.

I decided to focus my attention on that story and see where it led me.

I yearned for a record deal; I dreamt about it every night. A record deal was my number one life goal.

Dad started working remote, and my parents thought that my talent for songwriting might be better honed in Tennessee. I agreed, plus, I thought that a new school might be the fresh start my brother and I needed. Neither of us were having much luck with friends at school.

The Harmonía family said goodbye to our Christmas tree farm, friends, and Larry. We moved to the land of honkytonks and live country bands.

I remember following the moving van, along Highway 65, riding shotgun in Mom's black Denali. I was excited to see what my future held and experienced no premonition of the calamities to come.

I truly started with the purest intentions. I never set out to become an international superstar.

CHAPTER 5

KEY TO THE DREAM

"Most of us are still, in some small way, victims of the Industrial Revolution. We were raised to believe that our place in life required compliance and conformity rather than creativity and uniqueness. Whether this contrast was reinforced on an assembly line, in a cubicle, or in a classroom; the surest path to acceptance in society is accepting standardization. And we more than willingly relinquish our uniqueness."

Erwin Raphael McManus

Miss Weeks continued her story.

"Florence West perished in a tragic sail boat accident off the Rhode Island coast, just before her son, Allen, turned eighteen. You know, Angel, Allen never saw his father, Thomas, smile again.

Thomas West, Betty's grandfather, focused all of his attention on his work and eventually left his son with a vast financial and social legacy. Thomas retired as a respected and very wealthy man in St. Louis, Missouri. He gifted his son, Betty's father, with the keys to his kingdom.

Still, Thomas issued Allen a warning. "Make smart choices, boy; money comes, and money goes. Shirtsleeves to shirtsleeves in three generations."

The train tracks crossed in the center of St. Louis's downtown area, making the city a prime candidate for world events. In the years following Florence's death, the fierce lion of the valley hosted both the World's Fair and the Olympic games.

St. Louis made its acquaintance with tens of millions of new faces as the city captured the heart of American popular culture.

Judy Garland herself would later serenade Betty:

Meet me in St. Louis, Baby. Meet me at the fair.
Don't tell me the lights are shining any place but there.
We will dance the Hoochee Coochee;
I will be your Tootsie Wootsie.
If you will meet in St. Louis, Betty. Meet me at the fair.

Throughout the early twentieth century, businessmen across America drove cities towards peak industrialization. Hundreds of thousands transplanted to St. Louis during the Great Migration between World War I and World War II. Businesses and factories popped up on every corner. Opportunity was plentiful.

Over in Kitty Hawk, Orville and his brother completed a successful maiden voyage of the Wright Flyer, and people were beginning to imagine what it could be like to fly amongst the clouds. Manufacturers across the country began production of a new and very exciting invention, one that would change the world as we know it— the automobile.

St. Louis prided itself on being at the forefront of the newest inventions. America's first gas station was right down the street from Allen's estate.

A 21-year-old Allen West had no qualms about shelling out $1,500 for an open-sided, forest-green touring car from the St. Louis Motor Carriage company. He had one of the first cars in the city and masqueraded around the cobblestone streets in the driver's seat like it was his royal carriage.

As more people were able to afford automobiles, the roads became more dangerous than a Civil War battleground. There were few rules of the road. Drivers didn't know what they were doing... everyone drove recklessly.

Forty years later, Allen would tell Elizabeth Taylor and Richard Burton that he saw the world's first automobile accident occur right across the street from the Missouri Botanical Gardens.

By 1910, over half a million people lived in the little city Thomas West had taken over. The economy was booming. Thomas's son, Allen, and his childhood friends found themselves reigning over St. Louis.

Thanks to their parents' sizable inheritances, these young men were able to buy up everything that was worth owning in the city. They bought politicians like cattle. They invested in the media. They headed the boards of the biggest companies. They finagled a total monopoly on city resources.

When World War I began, these young men were also able to avoid the draft. Allen had no interest in following his veteran father's footsteps. His father never discussed the war, and Allen wasn't around to see how Thomas's army pension paved the way for the West family's prosperity. Allen did, however, take full advantage of the business opportunities that this conflict provided.

The city's economy and the fortunes of Allen and his friends handsomely benefited from the world war. St. Louis was one of the main manufacturing hubs for wartime industries. Glittering opportunity attracted people from all over the world.

Immigrants from Europe, former slaves migrating from the South, and plantation families who had never totally recovered from the Panic of 1837 moved in droves. All were seeking employment. As the population and workforce grew, tense competition was created for employment, housing, and public resources in the city— causing wages to go down and the cost of living to go up.

Supply and demand, Angel.

It didn't help, of course, that there was no federally-mandated minimum working wage in that day.

Rational businessmen took advantage of the opportunity that the flux in the workforce provided them. Their investors, like Allen and his friends, demanded more from their investment.

History repeats itself.

Once again, the businesses were able to compete with prices instead of quality. Once again, business owners realized that punishment was a greater incentive than reward.

This time, the wealthy were just pulling the strings while paying others to do the dirty work for them. Businesses around America cut wages and raised expectations for the productivity of their workers.

Allen, dressed sharply in a three-piece lounge suit, sat at the bar in the lobby of the St. Louis Athletic Club. There were no televisions at the time, so the closest thing Allen could get to watching his beloved Cardinals play in-person was watching the game at a bar. The club casted the game off to the side of the lobby; the boys watched as a tiny hand moved the little mechanical players around the wall as the players on the field ran to 1st, 2nd, 3rd, then home.

Allen and his unruly friends were the definition of a country club crew. They cheered when their team hit a pop fly and chanted like fraternity boys: "First in booze, first in shoes, and last in the American League!" Frothy beer spilled onto the bar as the men griped about labor unions and strikes.

Around the city, tensions grew. The factory workers, who were being pushed to their limits, began whispering about the same.

Business owners had no time for workplace tension, however. If a manager got wind of an employee who was ruffling feathers, that employee would be swiftly fired.

Workers became even more stressed. America was supposed to be about freedom, yet they found themselves enslaved by an unfair system.

Despite his privilege, Allen let many things rile him up. Allen began to develop a reputation. Whispered rumors flew about the city:

"Did you hear? That young West boy punched
the corner bum in the face."

"Allen West lost his temper on Mayor Wells and
got booted from City Hall."

"Don't play Allen in poker... he doesn't like to lose."

Angel, Allen's temperament got no more pleasant with age.

Back at the country club, the growing sect of young adults petitioned for more social activities. On a warm August evening, a gussied up Sternwheeler was booked to take the young club members up and down the Mississippi River. The club footed the bill, and the young guests took full advantage of the open bar.

All aboard!

A small group of young women had caught the eye of Allen and his friends. The girls giggled as the boys brought over a round of drinks. The riverboat drifted past bustling public markets and families having a picnic at the park. A Dixieland quartet played up-tempo jazz; their brass instruments sizzled from the glare of the setting August sun.

Allen had pulled the prettiest of the group to the dance floor: a tall, slender woman with short blonde hair and big blue eyes.

He asked her name. "Rebekah," she replied, coyly. "Rebekah Semple."

Allen spun Rebekah around the dance floor until the boat docked and the band began to pack their instruments into their cases. The couple then sat on the side of the boat, chatting animatedly, as a soft glow illuminated the young city in the distance. They stayed long after the other young folks had dissipated. Finally, the riverboat captain had to ask them to leave.

Allen walked Rebekah home.

He immediately realized that she could help him experience his life in a different way. Allen couldn't put his finger on exactly what it was about Rebekah he liked, but he knew she had to be his.

Allen shyly reached for her hand. Despite the growing evening chill, Rebekah's cheeks flushed as his fingers traced along hers.

Hands clasped, they walked along Seventh Street between Chestnut and Pine and marveled over the massive Wainwright skyscraper. Rebekah felt drunk from the hope of it all; giddy, with an excitement that sparked in their interlaced fingers and burrowed itself inside her heart.

What a beautiful time to be alive, she thought.

When Allen chose Rebekah, he was picking from the cream of the crop. The St. Louis Athletic Club had a rigorous admission criteria including a hand-written reference from two current members and a hefty admission fee of $50,000.

Mr. Semple, Rebekah's father, was a wealthy merchant, based out of Minneapolis... but it was only through her mother's connections that allowed them membership. Her mother's family, the Culbertsons, were a notoriously wealthy, old money family from Indiana.

When Rebekah turned sixteen, Mr. Semple moved his family and merchant business out of the Land of Lakes, to a city with more opportunity: St. Louis, Missouri.

Three years later, on the Mississippi River, Allen danced his way into Rebekah's life. He quickly took notice of the pleasant things about her. When she smiled, a pair of dimples crinkled themselves adorably into her cheeks. One day, he realized that he liked looking at the curve of her nose. It wasn't anything that he could really put his finger on or describe, but just being around Rebekah made him feel good. Allen could look at her all day.

He noticed how cute it was when she doing something difficult and her brow wrinkled just above the nose. He loved the way she laughed, with a genuine, full-body chortle, when he told a joke. He started to feel a little flutter in his chest every time Rebekah was around. When she kissed him goodbye, the feeling of her lips on his lingered for hours. His usually despondent daydreams transformed to a film reel of their happiest moments played back in terrific color.

Allen courted Rebekah for nine months. He bought her oysters at Tony Faust's. They danced at the hottest swing clubs and adopted a golden retriever named Cheddar. With Rebekah by his side, Allen felt like he could be anyone he wanted to be. They talked about their future family and made hushed promises about growing old together.

Allen Tarwater West was in love... a feeling he felt at every minute of every day. The boy who had everything wanted to marry Rebekah Semple.

Allen sent Rebekah's father a telegram expressing his intentions:

Mr. Semple,

I have gotten to know your daughter and our relationship has progressed quite quickly, in a way that would have taken years if we were not in a city. I love her, and I promise to take care of her. I intend to marry her. I'm hoping to have your approval.

Sincerely,
Allen West

With her father's understandably hesitant consent, Rebekah and Allen bought a ticket, packed their bags, and jostled along the bumpy rails straight to Minneapolis. Rebekah always dreamt of being married in the church where she grew up.

With Allen's arm around his fiancee's tiny waist, the couple whispered sweet nothings to each other on their journey. Time passed quickly. Before Rebekah knew it, it was wedding day.

Sunlight refracted through the stained glass windows in Rebekah's magnificent childhood church. Blue, red, green, and yellow prisms danced on the faces of well-wishers in the pews.

They stood for the bride.

A white, streamlined silhouette appeared. Arm in arm with her father, Rebekah began the descent towards her soon-to-be husband.

Allen stood at the alter. Sunlight from the windows above streamed onto him like a spotlight. His eyes were moist; they glistened as if they were made of tiny diamonds. As the wedding bells rang, two hundred of their closest family and friends threw handfuls of rice at the young lovebirds.

The new Mr. and Mrs. West spent a week with the extended Semple family in Minneapolis, after which they returned to St. Louis, ready to start their lives together.

With the dowry Rebekah's father had given Allen as a downpayment, the Wests purchased a massive red-brick, 42-room mansion on Westmoreland Place— the trendiest street in St. Louis for the nouveau riche. The Wests moved into one of the wings and put Allen's father, Thomas, in another. The third wing, which Rebekah had completely redesigned, featured various guest rooms and ample space to entertain St. Louis's high society.

The Wests had two children, both named after their parents. Both also went by nicknames: Betty, who came first, and Al. Their nannies kept the children busy when guests were around.

It was the roaring twenties and despite their growing family, the Wests sought to be the Gatsbys of St. Louis. Rebekah was a natural, charming host. Allen had a steady stock of alcohol despite the ongoing prohibition. He also had the police chief in his back pocket.

The Wests had no shortage of friends.

But as the Wests and their friends toasted to their good fortune, race riots were happening east of the river.

When the first world war started, much of the country's workforce had enlisted and left their towns and cities to fight. This temporarily eased workforce tensions... but when the war ended, already crowded cities became even more congested. Businesses, who at first were worried about staying afloat after the war, found an easy solution. St. Louis's supply of ready and willing workers increased... which of course decreased demand, alongside workers's wages and rights.

Tensions exploded.

Labor unions popped up across the city. Unions led to strikes. The entire economy and growth of our nation was disrupted. Factories, without workers to man the machines, were forced to put production on hold. Without goods to sell, the economy stalled.

Notorious for his terrible temper, Allen was a ruthless and cutthroat businessman. When his customers were affected by labor strikes, Allen suggested, "Just hire some Negros to replace those lazy bums."

St. Louis business owners, like thousands of others throughout the country, did just that. Black migrant workers were previously not considered worthy of paying money, and they often had to resort to undignified means in order to survive. Now, they were more than willing to capitalize on the opportunity provided.

My dear, Angel; although black people wouldn't be able to vote for another fifty years and were barely considered more than 3⁄5 of a person, companies found themselves eager to employ them... especially for pennies on the dollar.

Anything goes when it comes to their bottom line.

Allen and his friends, who had more money than they knew what to do with, had recently pooled their money to invest in a failing but once prosperous newspaper. They figured, if they controlled the news, they controlled a direct line into the minds of their populace.

That connection could be valuable.

Allen saw an opportunity in all of the workforce tension to test the power his new investment afforded him. He thought to himself, *those white factory workers need a new target for their anger.*

Allen conducted a social experiment. That Sunday, the headlines read:

New Negros: They're Out For Your Jobs! Beware!

Pitted against one another in such a visible manner, tensions went nuclear. White, mostly working-class Americans, once angry at the elites, now directed their anger at the Negros. Dressed in suits and house clothes, they calmly roamed the streets of predominately-black neighborhoods, ala the Purge, looking for black people to terrorize and massacre.

They weren't drunk, Angel. Nobody was needed to rile up the crowd. Their systematic manhunt was done for sport.

Businesses and homes were set on fire, sometimes with people trapped inside. A little black baby, who moments before had been torn from his wailing mother's arms, was thrown into a burning building. A group of white women with baseball bats above their heads encircled a cowering group of black women who were shielding their heads with battered arms.

Two black men, weakened from a brutal, tortuous beating, were hung on a clothesline by their shirts. The crowd was still milling about when one of the men's shirts slipped from the clothes pins, and he crumpled onto the ground. Barely conscious, he was hung from a tree with a noose.

After three long days, during which black families fled the city— literally running for their lives— the massacre ended. Two hundred and fifty were dead. Countless injuries were sustained. Six thousand were left displaced or homeless from the burning and the vandalism.

Nobody was ever held accountable for the riots.

Here we are again, Angel, in the same winner-take-all, anything-goes environment that fostered the brutalities of cotton slavery.

The common-folk were starving. Unemployment levels were high. Homeless camps appeared overnight in empty lots and under old bridges. Businesses, many of which were seeing exponential growth in revenue, failed to pay their laborers a livable wage. The government had not yet stepped in to regulate.

America was beginning to experience a true tragedy of the commons.

Allen and his friends were living in a cut throat world. Everyone employed a similar mantra: *grow or die.*

This kind of environment is inevitably toxic. Surely it will lead to decisions that detract from the more noble pursuit of greater good.

To escape life's tragic reality, many of these wealthy young people threw massive parties in sea-side homes and sprawling mansions.

The West family took the train east to ease their mind of racial tensions, the economy, and politics. They traveled all night by train for long weekend trips to their little saltbox house on the Atlantic Coast in Watch Hill, Rhode Island.

Watch Hill is a timeless coastal village on the most southwest point in The Ocean State. Watch Hill's rambling roads reveal whimsical summer cottages which boast expansive cobblestone driveways, wide, wrap around porches, and softly rolling lawns.

Watch Hill residents were members of some of America's most affluent families. Some descended from the men who had served as lookouts on the bluff during the Revolutionary War. Others were descendants of Mayflower pilgrims.

All were addicted to the serenity, white sand, and hazy views of Long Island across the way. Many soon became addicted to the tennis and golf scene at the Watch Hill Country Club.

Given its name largely due to its historical significance, Watch Hill was used as a key lookout point in both the French and Indian and the Revolutionary Wars. Allen's father, Thomas, had originally purchased their seaside property just a few years after founding the St. Louis Trust Company.

General Forrest brought his troops through Watch Hill during the Civil War. Thomas heard folklore of the rich and heroic history of the area. Thomas was eager to become one of the first residential builders on the bluff. He also served as the town's first mayor.

The West family felt like they were somebodies in Watch Hill. Their story was foundational; generational. Betty's grandfather, Thomas, was now sick and could no longer make the long trips east; but the Wests maintained their status as core members of Watch Hill society. Their family legacy was valuable; they were part of the establishment. Despite the resources Allen controlled back in St. Louis, the Wests were never able to achieve the same social status in the big city they called home.

Allen would join his wife, Rebekah, for a nightly stroll past gilded mansions and sprawling sea-side farmhouses. The couple reveled in the shadow of Holiday House: the biggest home in Watch Hill which loomed boldly from the bluff after which the town was named. Despite its enormous size, Holiday House only added to the discreet charm of this New England town.

Allen couldn't even dream of owning it.

Allen liked Watch Hill just fine, but it didn't have the glitz and glamour of the Hamptons, for example. His family's place in Watch Hill was nowhere close to being as big as his mansion in St. Louis; but it was still very beautiful, and only about a half mile from the beach. Rebekah cherished every minute they spent in that little town. Watch Hill provided a welcome distraction from the life she had constructed for herself in St. Louis.

One weekend, the Johnson family, of St. Louis's International Shoe Company fortune, joined the Wests out East. The two families walked along Rhode Island's rocky shoreline, cocktails in tow. They were on their way to the beach by the lighthouse for a sunset picnic.

The grown-ups drank and laughed while they watched a scattering of pink and golden hues reflect in fiery shades upon the water. Golden hour quickly faded to dusk.

Jane Johnson was seven, the same age as Allen and Rebekah's daughter, Betty. The two girls ran back and forth to the water, digging their toes in the sandy banks searching for sand dollars beneath the surface. The girls never tired of their quest... collecting more and more sand dollars. They only stopped once the cocktails had been finished, the picnic basket packed, and their nannies had reined them in.

Later that night, Jane and Betty stayed up long after their parents had gone to sleep; their whispers and hushed giggles were drowned out by the roar of the Atlantic.

Back in St. Louis, Allen and Mr. Johnson went duck hunting every Saturday morning while their wives drank mimosas and discussed books their husbands didn't want them to be reading... like *The Jungle*, a book that had been banned in most schools and libraries.

Painting a tragic picture that was a striking contrast from her own charmed reality, Upton Sinclair completely changed Mrs. Johnson's perception of the world. Dismayed by the horrors of the meat packing industry, Jane's mother transitioned the Johnson family into vegetarianism. She neglected to realize that her family's wealth, gained by the exploitation of the system, only contributed to the problems exposed by that book.

While their mothers were busy hosting book club, Jane and Betty took horseback riding lessons at the Johnson's 13-acre horse stable, ballet lessons at the premier St. Louis studio, and partied with children from St. Louis's most prominent families. They had a very privileged view of the world; still, they were not blind to what was going on around them.

Jane snuck into her mother's room and read *The Jungle* when she wasn't looking. Jane was also horrified after reading the book... but in a different way than her mother. Little Jane somehow knew, intuitively, that the story did not originate from an isolated incident.

She and Betty discussed; something was terribly wrong with the world around them.

The girls were young, though, and didn't know much about anything anyways. *Young women don't have the capacity to understand economics,* people thought. *They're much better suited for 4H: mastering the art of womanhood, motherhood, and wife-hood.* Betty and Jane rebelled against that notion.

This was America. Betty wanted the freedom to live any type of life she wanted.

In the years to come, Betty West would have her turn to dance, of course... but, the laws of nature will always reign supreme.

Before the end of the Industrial Revolution, capitalism's problem of limited supply was replaced by the problem of limited demand. Industrial economies could produce an endless supply of goods. Unless purchasing power was widely distributed and continuously rising, there would soon be too few people with the capacity to procure them.

America needed to figure out how to fix the issues with demand.

Economists, such as Marshall and then Keynes, shifted their focus from the supply side of the equation to demand. Their work gave rise to a new set of economic principles, some of which still guide public policy today.

But, my dear Angel; in the quest of limitless growth, we lost sight of a larger issue. Unlimited capacity for production would inevitably tax and destroy the Earth's finite resources.

Maybe we should have been asking ourselves, *what type of growth is it that we want?* or *what will lead the collective to our overarching goal of greater good?* Instead, the attention was focused on stimulating demand to keep pace with the growth of production."

Miss Weeks paused.

In the years that followed, the nanny would get a front-row seat to the spectacle of Betty's grandfather's proverb playing out.

Shirtsleeves to shirtsleeves in three generations.

Or sooner… Miss Weeks thought to herself.

CHAPTER 6

NASHVILLE

"Education is not the learning of facts,
but training the mind to think."
Albert Einstein

I didn't set out to become an international superstar but have since realized that becoming a superstar was the exact crux of my problem.

I became too big of a force, and nothing is ever what it seems... not on stage and not in life.

My family moved to Nashville, and I started freshman year at Phroneis— a private high-school, downtown, that is a five-minute walk from Centennial Park. My brother was at the middle school on the other side of the park.

Equipped with fresh highlights, new shoes, and a positive attitude, I was ready to take on high school. I was also ready to make the Nashville music scene my bitch. Metaphorically speaking, of course.

One of the first lessons I learned in high school was that of crucial importance:

The order of nature is based on a balance of rights and obligations; a golden equilibrium that results when the primary opposites act as equals.

The tension of opposites, I thought, as I remembered the story of Aphrodite.

Of course, I didn't understand the complexities of Sir Newton's statement back then… I was too enthralled with the happenings of Phroneis High. Despite the Friday night lights, Monday morning pep rallies, and cardboard cafeteria pizza, high school was like nothing I could have imagined. New to town, I think I appeared to everyone… mysterious? For the first time in my life, I felt sparkly and interesting around kids my own age.

I now know those sparkly feelings were largely a mirage; I was just a novelty. Everyone at Phroneis had gone to school together since kindergarten. They were bored with one another. In this type of environment, new kids get attention. Mysterious new girls are on the receiving end of the type of attention I had never experienced before.

Girls wanted to be my friend. For the first time in my life boys were interested in me, too.

I'm a hopeless romantic. I've always loved *love* ever since I was a little girl.

I study people who are in love, people who have fallen out of love, and people who have found love again. I've lost days of my life thinking about the ways humans interact with one another, and the crazy way that one person can feel one way and another can feel something totally different.

Boys had ignored me in Pennsylvania, so all of my love stories were housed in my imagination. When a cute, senior hockey player asked me to dinner at Olive Garden, I thought it might be my turn for love in real life.

Hockey boy waited for me in the morning by my locker. One day, he brought me flowers. Just because. All the other freshman girls noticed.

"Be careful, Rae! You keep getting flowers, and you won't have any friends... they will all be too jealous," my new friend, Abbe, said with a giggle.

Still, I never felt more like I belonged. *Finally,* I thought, *I fit into the picture the rest of the world is painting.*

Life was good.

I lived in country music heaven, I dated a senior on the hockey team, and I marketed myself constantly up and down Music Row. I sang in bars and cafes; I met interesting, well-connected people.

Then, hockey boy and I broke up after a few months. I didn't have much time for him, anyways, when focusing on music. Plus, I was a good girl, so I wouldn't take my clothes off... no matter how many times he asked.

I made some friends. I lost some friends.

I played a song I wrote at Phroneis's talent show and dedicated it to Abbe's ravishing older brother on a dare. I saw him leave the auditorium in the middle of my song, embarrassed. I reddened on stage, mortified.

More and more people started to listen to, and like, my music, though. The little shows I played at the park and at family parties, turned into concerts at neighborhood festivals and church cookouts. Sometimes four or five hundred people were in the crowd!

Abbe taught me about Myspace. She kept the number one position on my 'Top Friends' list, as my friend count went from twenty to twenty thousand. I could interact with my fans directly on Myspace and found that I related to many of them more than the kids I went to school with.

I've finally found people that understand the real me.

I finally found people that liked the real me.

I started playing at bigger and bigger venues. I strummed and sang at a karaoke bar in Nashville each week. I wrote love songs; mostly from those stories housed deep within my imagination. I quickly realized, though, the boys at Phroneis High were not like the ones I dreamt of... especially the senior ones.

I look back and see the same story repeat, over and over. A boy asked me for my phone number. We texted back and forth for days or maybe weeks. Things would start to get steamy; but then, just fizzle.

Time after time, the details changed only slightly with each reprise. Like a shooting star... one moment we'd shine bright, and the next we'd disappear into the black abyss of the universe.

I began to feel more like a shiny, mysterious object that everyone just wanted a piece of. It was the first time I had consciously felt this way, but it would certainly not be the last.

As women, it is constantly reinforced, consciously and subconsciously, that we are just here to fulfill other's wants and desires. We're idolized for our parts. Many don't care for the whole.

Mom and I sat at the kitchen table every day after school. I told her about my problems. She told me stories and tried to teach me lessons. She reminded me, "The light inside of you is brighter than all the lights in New York City."

Still, I felt disjointed.

How could I be the person I wanted to be?

Mom stroked my hair. "Baby, stories are all we are."

She was right. I needed to take control and write my own story. My family moved to Nashville for a reason.

I reverted my attention back to school and my music. School helped me create; I learned so many interesting things and that knowledge helped me open Pandora's box.

Knowledge is power, they say.

Song-writing became my story-telling weapon of choice.

English has always been my favorite subject. In freshman literature, Mr. Hillman had us read the classics: *To Kill a Mockingbird, Alice's Adventures in Wonderland*, and *1984*. Even still, I feel that I have more to learn from them... I can't shake it off.

Mr. Hillman used *To Kill a Mockingbird* to show our class the ways that deeper meaning can be woven into classic literature. Literature models myth in that way.

The story teaches about innocence and civility. Harper Lee's overarching theme— to never stray from kindness and compassion, no matter where life leads you— lingers in my subconscious today.

Sometimes, when I got older and couldn't sleep, Mom would read me *Alice's Adventures in Wonderland.* I was enchanted by the tale of magic, danger, and adventure; of a girl who is burning with curiosity and tumbles down a rabbit hole.

Mr. Hillman helped me see Alice's story in a totally new way; he taught me that Lewis Carroll was actually an esteemed mathematician, and that his seemingly childish tales draw on complex ideas of the nature of language, truth, and logic.

There's deeper meaning to be found in Alice, too; like in the parable of the Walrus and the Carpenter, told to Alice by Tweedle-dee and Tweedle-dum. In the story, the Walrus met some oysters on the beach and invited them to a feast. The oysters agreed and, together, they walked along the shore towards their picnic destination.

The oysters soon realized, however, that the feast would involve them getting eaten. They cried, "Please, Mr. Walrus, don't eat us!"

The Walrus talked nonsense to distract them. Then, he ate the oysters, one by one.

When the Walrus was finished with his meal, he started back to the place he came from. "Oysters," he called out, "come forth and give me company on my walk."

But, there were none. Without even realizing it, the Walrus had eaten every last one.

George Orwell's *1984* is a dystopian novel that dives into the realities of a world predicted— where the Ministry of Truth lies; the Ministry of Peace wages war; the Ministry of Love tortures. As if written by a man with a time machine,

1984 is a mockery of truth and a creative display of the tension of opposites.

Mr. Hillman taught me an important life lesson: analyzing literature can tune your critical thinking skills so that you better understand the truths about the world around you. Sometimes, revisiting the classics is the best way to do so... no matter how old you are or how well you think you know the story.

Poetry, even more than literature, spoke to me as if it were whispering in a secret tongue. Mr. Hillman also taught me to analyze some of time's greatest poets: Shakespeare, Yeats, Plath, Blake, Keats.

Like a master teacher, poetry refined my ability to puzzle words together to form meaning, context, imagery, and effect. It was only by breaking a poem down into its parts, that I learned how stories are woven together— in beautiful patterns. Each pattern tells a different story, sometimes not immediately understood. I noticed how the stories embedded in my favorite poetry had an inevitable impact on the way I saw the world.

The second Tuesday of August, Mr. Hillman began our freshman lit class by lecturing about numbers. I was puzzled. Math was my least favorite subject; I didn't want it to spoil my favorite one. I still remember the lesson, though, like it was yesterday.

Mr Hillman's resonant voice lingers in my memory. "My interest in numbers was sparked long ago. Right out of school, I taught third grade. The school was called Horace Greeley, in Chicago, IL. Like any good teacher, I tried not to leave my pupils' questions unanswered— no matter how odd or silly of a question it seemed."

He paused. "I've always believed that a curious mind is an intelligent one."

Mr. Hillman continued, "My literature concentration in college gave me a somewhat divergent approach to teaching. Fresh out of school, I had big dreams. Before teaching my little third graders about arithmetic, I would teach them the *significance of numbers* in hopes of better capturing their attention. I told the children that numbers have mystified people throughout the ages; a fascination that can be seen as early as in cavemen's hieroglyphics..." He trailed off.

"...and it was at about that point in the lesson, when one of the kids asked a question that was so innocent, yet it nearly knocked me off my feet."

My teacher's deep voice rose in pitch imitating a small child.

"*Mr. Hillman!* A little girl in the front row was waving her hand ferociously in the air. *But, where do numbers come from? Like, who invented the number zero?*"

He looked at us for a moment, incredulous.

"I stared at her, dumbfounded. I was prepared to change these kids' lives with the significance of numbers, yet, I never thought of that very simple yet fundamental question myself. Who did invent numbers?"

Mr. Hillman continued, "I went home and did some research. I read textbook after textbook, journal after journal. All of the research was pointing me towards the same place, however, into the unknown."

"Into the universe..." he trailed off.

Okay, Mr. Hillman... I'm intrigued.

At home, after school, I did some research of my own.

An ancient air of mystery, surrounding the significance of numbers, has burrowed itself across the time and space boundary; in music, art, architecture, and literature. I read about an Ancient Greek thinker, Pythagoras, who thought that numbers were the basis of the entire universe. He believed that the universe operated according to natural laws that could be understood through numerical harmony.

Throughout time, numbers have acted as the mediators between cosmic phenomena and human everyday life. This can be observed by studying etymology: the study of the origin of words, and the way their meanings have maintained or transformed throughout time.

For example, we could look at the etymology of the words chosen for the days of the week. They are similar throughout time and culture. In almost all languages, their names were coined with inspiration from the seven celestial objects originally considered to be planets— the Sun, the Moon, Mars, Mercury, Jupiter, Venus, and Saturn.

Maybe numbers do carry some mystical, cosmic significance, I thought.

History, taught by Mr. Wade, tied right into my investigations.

Mr. Wade was tall and lean. He had the deep, booming voice of a Greek god.

Looking back, it is clear; like Mr. Hillman, Mr. Wade understood something special about teaching. He knew that the key to understanding lay near the beginning. On the first day of school, Mr. Wade taught us about Herodotus.

Herodotus changed the game of history and the world as we know it. He was the first to write history down in story form. Before Herodotus, history was just gathered via ordinal lists, with no attempts to connect dots. Conversely, his book, *Histories*, attempted to give a storied version of history.

Histories is the OG[5] history book— our oldest record of history. It's largely what all other history books are based off of; thus, what our idea of history is based off of.

Histories begins with:

Herodotus of Halicarnassus. Here lie his inquires.

For the first time, a true, historical story was pieced together using inquiry and reason as opposed to pure fact. Herodotus traveled around the Persian empire collecting folktales, first-hand accounts, and traditions from different cultures.

Herodotus prophesied, *when history is told as stories, humankind can learn from the mistakes of the past.*

That sounds true enough.

Hundreds of years later, though, people still can't decide what to call Herodotus; the 'Father of History,' or the 'Father of Lies.' You never know how history will write your story… even if you're the one writing history.

Life's funny like that.

Over the years, I've seen how time can change one's story in an instant.

---

5 "OG" is a 90's trend that has adapted over time. It was originally the abbreviation for "Original Gangster." Now, it is typically used to mean, "original."

At school, I quickly lost the luster of mystical new girl. The more I withdrew from the high-school-social-scene and the more I dove into songwriting and my music, the less people liked me. Phroneis High felt like a snake pit as whispers hissed around campus.

I thanked my lucky stars, each night, for my best friend, Abbe.

Mom signed me up for music lessons. A washed-up 'country legend' taught me valuable lessons about showmanship, story-telling, and singing with a Southern twang. I brought my unlined notebook and an ink-well-pen to take notes during our sessions.

Dad booked me at different cafes and bars around Nashville. After school, I walked up and down Music Row passing out demo tapes. My after-school work uniform was a sundress and cowboy boots. My name-tag was my platinum smile.

"Hi! I'm Rae!" I beamed at the blonde secretary... or if I was lucky, a record label executive. I dropped a demo tape off at each record label on the historic Music Row. Again.

Finally, this time, my hard work started to pay off. A few big labels called— Universal, Epic. Then, Dad heard from an independent label— Friends Keep Secrets.

None of them were ready to offer me what I really wanted, though. I would only sign with a label that let me record my own music. I wanted to be able to tell my own stories.

Dad agreed. "Rae, you're the perfect person to dominate an incredibly profitable, niche market. We just need to find you the right deal."

He was right, of course. I was a teenage girl. All my friends were teenage girls. Who better to write songs for teenage girls?

One day, Dad told me he booked me to perform at the legendary Bluebird Cafe— an iconic Nashville venue that had boosted some of my idols to super-stardom. I spent hours obsessing over the perfect songs to perform.

A few days before the gig, I walked to Centennial Park after school. I was on the quest for answers. Red and golden leaves rained on me as the fall wind whipped through the park's lush oasis. As I walked near the water, a chill tickled my spine. I wrapped my wool scarf tighter around my neck.

I walked towards the center of the park, near the Parthenon: a full scale replica of the Ancient Greek temple. The original Parthenon was built in 438 B.C. by Phidias, as a memorial to the goddess of wisdom, Athena. The Parthenon in Centennial Park was constructed in 1897 as part of the Tennessee Centennial Exposition and to celebrate Nashville as the 'Athens of the South.'

Inside the replica lives a 42-foot tall sculpture of Athena. I stood in her shadow, closed my eyes, and pictured the bright lights shining on me and my guitar on stage at Bluebird. I took a deep breath, and my vision changed. There I was, signing a record deal, in a velvet padded office with a pen made of pure gold. I took another breath. Now, I was headlining a concert; singing back to thousands of screaming fans.

I took another deep breath.

Everything was going to be alright.

For Bluebird, I chose three songs: all originals and all about heartbreak.

Heartbreak tends to be a crowd-pleaser. It's relatable.

I practiced in front of my mirror, then my family, then Dad's old tape recorder. Afterwards, I popped the VHS in the TV and watched, re-wound, then re-watched my tapes. I analyzed my every move.

Bluebird needs to go perfectly, I thought.

The day finally arrived.

I made it through school, barely. Abbe and I walked home together after school. Then, I changed into my favorite sundress. I clicked my cowboy boots, three times, like Dorothy.

It's showtime.

I blink; suddenly, I'm back on the stage at Bluebird sitting on a stool in the dark.

The lights came up.

"Hi y'all, I'm Rhea Harmonía... most of my friends call me Rae!"

I flashed the audience my platinum smile and paused.

As my eyes adjusted to the lights, I first searched for my parents. They were in the back row beaming. We decided that it would be better for the talent agents and scouts to have closer seats.

My eyes scanned the rest of the crowd and were drawn to a man, dressed in all black, sitting smack dab in the center. He was nursing a cup of coffee and furiously writing in a notebook. We made eye contact.

My smile widened; I ramped up my charm.

"I'm so happy that y'all decided to join me here at Bluebird on this beautiful Thursday evening. I wrote a couple of songs that I'd like to play for you tonight. If you enjoy them, come say hi after the show. My mom and dad are sitting towards the back… hey Mom and Dad," I giggled and waved like I practiced.

I brushed the curls out of my eyes, then continued. "We just moved to Nashville so I could focus on my music career. I'm fifteen and a freshman at Phroneis High. I actually wrote this first song at Phroneis in math class…" I trailed off, dramatically.

I shielded my eyes and searched the crowd, then continued, "Hopefully Miss Swink isn't out there tonight…"

The crowd chuckled, as I took a deep breath. I strummed my guitar, then began to sing.

As I sang, I scanned the crowd and saw that familiar, transfixed look wash over their faces. They were so happy.

I think they really like me.

My eyes were drawn back to the man sitting in the center of the cafe. He wasn't taking notes anymore; he was hypnotized.

After the show, he came up to introduce himself. "Toró," he said his name was, then handed Dad a jet black business card. "I think you are exactly what I have been looking for, Kid."

We chatted a few moments longer before I got pulled away to talk to others. Out of the corner of my eye, I watched as Toró pulled Dad aside. When the men parted, it was with a handshake.

Dad couldn't have known... but he had just made a deal with the devil.

Friday morning, I walked into the doors of Phroneis High excited about my future. I told Abbe about Bluebird. I brought Torò's thick, embossed business card to school, to show her. "That's really fancy," she said, with a giggle.

In first period, math, we learned about the Pythagorean Theorem[6]. In third period, the cute guy in jazz band passed me his number.

I was on the top of the world.

There was a storm brewing, however, deep within the oceans of my destiny. I looked out the window of the band room. It was raining.

I thought, *everything is going to be alright.*

I was wrong.

6 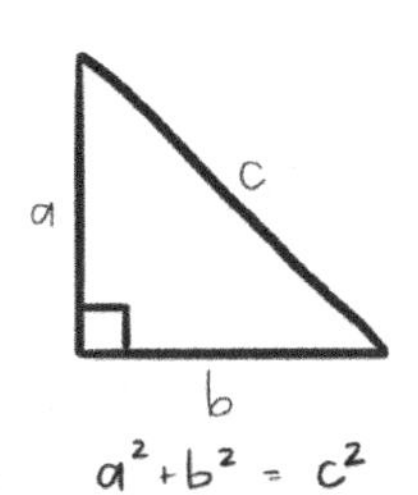

CHAPTER 7

BETTY WEST

"I know it when I see it."

U.S. Supreme Court Justice, Potter Stewart

Miss Weeks continued her story.

"Humans are social creatures. Love is a basic human need. If someone's basic needs aren't met, they may lack a fundamental pillar of being. They may have no hope of realizing their actualized self.

For many, family strengthens that crucial pillar; others aren't so lucky.

Sometimes, it may be this simple: a lack of love. Maybe others let their egos get in the way, obstructing their ability to give the people they love the love they need. It may be harder for those who weren't loved the right way as children to grow up to give that love to anyone else.

Human connection is of utmost importance across the lifespan. After childhood, when that connection is no longer built in, a person has to make choices. What will help give them that fundamental sense of belonging? Many turn to friend groups, romantic partners, hobbies, or work to fill that void.

Others turn to their shadow.

The column supporting Betty's feelings of 'love and belonging,' was made out of 24-karat gold. From far away it glistened; but as you got closer, you could see the gold was filled with cracks. In some places, portions of the pillar had crumbled away entirely.

Aimlessly, subconsciously yearning for more, Betty ran into a common mistake. She then, let that mistake repeat itself in her story over and over again.

She mistook attention for love.

All Betty ever wanted to do was find love. Now Angel, Betty's parents loved her, of course. But they loved money, firstly; then, more importantly, themselves. Her father was always working or off losing his temper. Her mother was always off in her own little world... usually drinking.

Their children, though, were taken care of by the best nannies St. Louis had to offer. Rare was there a want they went without. The West children always had the newest toys and nicest clothes. They took the most expensive lessons: Mondays were for ballet, Tuesdays for piano, Wednesdays were art, Thursdays were for sculpting, and on Saturdays, Betty took horseback riding. On warm summer Sundays in Watch Hill, a friend of her grandfather taught Betty to sail.

The West family was lucky enough to travel the world. Always riding in first class, whether they traveled by train or by boat, Betty experienced some of life's finer luxuries... both at home and abroad. As she got older, a personal chauffeur took her and Jane to and from school and wherever else they wanted to go.

What Betty's parents didn't give Betty, however, is the attention that she so desperately craved. They didn't tuck her in at night or read her stories. They didn't drop her off at lessons or meet instructors. They showed up late for her dance recitals. Once her father was so late, he completely missed her performance. Thinking she hadn't noticed, he lied between his teeth. "You danced like a prima ballerina!" he exclaimed, as the corners of his mouth lifted upwards obscenely; his face contorted itself into a smile.

The large size of the West's estate only exacerbated the neglect. Betty's parents spent a majority of their time in their 'apartment,' which was on an entirely different floor than Betty's room. Days would go by without Betty seeing her parents in person. A few weeks may have passed without Betty hearing the words, "I love you."

Early on, Betty learned that she got more attention when she was naughty... even if that attention was just in the form of a scolding from her old nanny.

In the first grade, Betty told her new friends that the nanny had worked in an insane asylum before coming to the West's house. This wasn't entirely true, however. Her nanny actually had been employed as a nurse in a local Home for the Elderly and Inferm.

The nanny told the children stories about her job: of a fifty year-old man-child who could easily be confused for an albeit big infant and of nude patients rolling themselves up and down the hallways.

Catch me if you can!

When Betty did something especially naughty— like the time she dipped the tip of another little girl's ponytail in her inkwell and the Principal called home— her father yelled at her.

Allen West looked terrifying when he was upset; his face writhed into that of a devilish stranger. He transformed into a curious shade of purple that reminded Betty of the eggplants growing in the garden the nanny kept on the side of their house. Betty didn't like being yelled at, of course... but it was nice to get some genuine, undivided attention on her every once in a while.

Betty wasn't the prettiest child, and she was self-conscious as sin.

She would never have been considered ugly, with parents like Allen and Rebekah. "Baby fat," her mother diagnosed it, with a disappointed sigh, in conversations about Betty with her friends.

Betty had thick, brown hair and a round, pudgy face. There was a tragically beautiful sense about her. When you looked into her big, opal eyes, there was something about them that made yours linger for a few extra moments.

Jane, Betty's best friend, was the opposite. She was a classic, blonde-haired-blue-eyed, Anglo-Saxon beauty. When someone as much as glanced at Jane, it was impossible for them to look away. As a baby, people stopped Jane's parents on the street to tell them, "Your little girl looks like a real-life angel!" When she was older, Jane's striking features and grandfather's last name landed her the cover of a national kids' fashion magazine. Her father framed the magazine cover to be hung on the wall in his office.

Jane's grandfather had just finished construction on the biggest factory in the city. His son, Jane's father, had the largest corner office on the third floor. From his perch above the city, Mr. Johnson enjoyed a birds's eye view of St. Louis's red, brick Main Street. He counted tiny horses, who pulled buggies, and trotted alongside sputtering automobiles.

Largely due to footwear needed for the war, the International Shoe Company had produced and sold 70 million pairs of shoes the past year. For Jane's family, business had never been better.

Betty's family wealth was also seeing exponential growth. During the past ten years, Thomas West's St. Louis Trust Company had become one of the city's most successful financial institutions.

Betty cared little for her fancy things... she saw the love Jane got from her parents and was jealous. Trying to make sense of the senseless world around her, she concluded: *it's always easier to find love when you're pretty.*

Betty became obsessed with the way she looked... she often stopped to study her reflection when she caught a glimpse of it in a store window or mirror. She had a recurring dream in which she woke to find that her baby fat had all melted off overnight. Little Betty lived her days for bed-time; her dreams were so much sweeter than her reality.

Betty did, in fact, grow up to be quite pretty— if only in a tall, athletic sense. She became slender, with long brunette hair, dramatic features, and mildly tanned skin. By the time she was a teenager, Betty was characterized by her icy blue eyes and spitfire spirit. The overwhelming consensus about her best friend, however, was more simple.

Jane was considered a classic beauty.

Betty and Jane ruled over their fancy private school like their families ruled over the city. In Constance's sacred, ivy-covered oasis, just across the street from the park, the girls filled their days with home-economics and private music lessons.

They wore plaid uniforms, knee high stockings, and shiny black penny loafers. In the uniforms, the girls were as indistinguishable as their upbringings.

These girls all came from wealth; so money didn't mean everything. Jane ruled over the school. None of the other girls could compare to the beautiful blonde's easy confidence and allure.

Betty was Jane's best friend; so, Betty was strapped in for the ride. To the outside observer, Betty got through school with ease. Other children stressed about humiliating themselves in front of their classmates or being pushed down on the playground. Betty, on the other hand, never sat alone at the lunch table. She did feel, however, as if she had to try a little harder than everyone else to fit in.

Betty always did quite well with her academics... though, it seemed that even Betty's teachers liked Jane more than her. Jane, with her quick tongue and curious mind, asked thought-provoking questions in class. Jane baked prettier pies than Betty in home-ec. In virtually every aspect of life, Jane was better; Jane got the most attention.

Betty often felt less than Jane. *Maybe,* Betty thought to herself, *I was just born to be Jane's less smart, less cool, and less attractive sidekick.* To compensate, Betty resorted to her old tactics to get attention. If Jane was an angel, then Betty would play the role of the devil.

Betty devised a motto: *do everything bad.*

When she brought that persona home, she learned quickly that her father was easily triggered. After a few incidents of having friends over, in which her father contorted himself into an eggplant, none of the little girls wanted to come play at her house anymore... even when her father wasn't home. Jane told her that she had heard a rumor whispered about school:

Betty West's house is haunted.

"Your dad is always so mad," Jane tried to explain; "that must be why!"

When they finished grade school, Betty and Jane, like many other girls from their class, were sent to finishing school. The Wests's chauffeur drove the girls and their stacks of luggage from St. Louis to South Carolina. The Duesenberg sputtered through South Boundary's magnolia tree tunnel towards the school.

Fermata School for the Girls was an expensive boarding school, housed in a large estate in Aiken, right off of Whiskey Road. Fermata educated the daughters of some of America's wealthiest families. Betty bunked alongside Jane, a Roosevelt, an Auchincloss, and tobacco heiress, Doris Duke.

Despite the tremendous wealth of some of their classmates, Betty and Jane fit in easily at Fermata. They had really grown into themselves; especially Jane. Jane's charisma caused girlfriends to flock to their side.

Ever-seeking attention, Betty continued her mischievous streak. Living in such close corridors with these girls, she felt constant pressure to do more to impress. Betty began acting more and more outrageous.

At parties with the boys' school, Betty would boldly turn off the lights and announce, with a coy smile, "Seven minutes in heaven!" She put whoopee cushions on her teachers' chairs. She convinced one classmate that her eyelashes would grow longer if she cut them off first.

Betty was voted funniest girl in the class, twice. A group of younger girls started following her around studying her every move. One day, Betty came to an astonishing realization: she was the one adored by the masses.

Stories floated around Fermata.

Betty metamorphosed into a legend.

She and Jane relished in the extra attention. Now, they had a more exclusive group of girlfriends... all of whom were intelligent, curious, and beautiful. With Betty in charge, the girls learned the power of their shadow. They referred to themselves as the Bitch Pack.

Jane brought back some books from her mother's extensive home library— books that had been banned by Fermata, like *On the Origin of Species* and *The Beautiful and the Damned*. She and Betty would hide the books under their pillows in the cold dorm and wait until their eyes had adjusted to the darkness. Then, they squinted at the small print and used the glow of the moon to try to piece together their thoughts on the world.

Betty and the Bitch Pack had heated discussions about injustice out of earshot of their fathers, of course, who had forbidden such talk. Jane devoured the fat newspaper that was delivered to campus each Sunday and informed the rest of the pack of the misfortunes happening in the world around them.

The stock market had just crashed. The girls peered at grainy, black and white photos depicting the tragedies of America's current reality: a long line of men, wearing suits and ties, stood single-file as they patiently waited in line for a free lunch at a local soup kitchen. A large plume of dust rose over the farmlands of the Great Planes. A desolate, dirty looking squatter family posed in front of their temporary housing shanty.

When they drove to Fermata, Betty and Jane saw more of America than they ever had before. As they passed through Chattanooga, rows and rows of small, dilapidated houses— scattered in insane disorder— whizzed past their eyes.

The driver called the encampments 'Hoovervilles,' and told the girls about a family he knew that was living in one.

"The kids' father, Frank, lost his job. One day, the factory let him go, without warning. The family had a little money saved up; but to stretch money even further, Frank waited in the two hour line at the soup kitchen each day for lunch.

"Before losing his job, Frank won a few pounds of coffee beans in a company raffle. If he drank one watery cup of coffee in the morning and another at night, he didn't even think about his growling stomach. The family's savings went towards feeding Frank's wife and their children.

"Still, money got used up real quick. Frank couldn't afford to pay his mortgage. Three months passed and the bank tacked a **FORECLOSURE** sign on their front door. He came home from the soup kitchen the next day and found his family's belongings dumped on the curb.

"Frank's beautiful wife stood there, despondent, a small child on each hip."

The car passed another shanty town, then another. Betty and Jane felt a pit grow in their stomachs: a feeling they had yet to identify as privilege.

Prohibition was over. That summer, seven-hundred guests had shown up to Jane's coming-out party; they each dined on a leg of lamb and partook in the open bar. Betty's family summered at their sea-side cottage in Watch Hill; they de-stressed on the soft, Rhode Island sand. Her parents partied with Gatsby on the coast.

As their worlds grew, Betty and Jane came to a grim realization; their parents' carefully constructed world was *not* reality. Reality, for most people, was tragic.

Betty and Jane were the lucky ones; their lives went on as normal. The only difference Betty noticed involved her father... he was now drinking a full glass of scotch each night after dinner. When Allen drank, he got even angrier.

It was like he knew: the world being built was but a house of cards.

On the eve of the Great Depression, Betty and Jane competed for the Queen of Love and Beauty at the Veiled Prophet's Ball— St. Louis's most anticipated philanthropy event of the year. Betty and Jane, both active members of the St. Louis Junior League, helped decorate Kiel Auditorium for the party. Hazy green, purple, and golden gauze was draped across the ceiling, intertwined with small twinkling lights.

The decoration committee had been going for a *magical, mardi-gras, masquerade* vibe.

Betty was giddy with delight when she received the telegram informing her of the prestigious nomination; yet, soon felt her spirits sink, when she heard that Jane had also been nominated.

Jane was going to win the crown. Betty just knew it.

Despite the new-found attention at Fermata, Betty still felt inferior to Jane. The gossip column in the local newspaper talked about the two girls frequently. The headlines had caused feelings of 'less-than' to manifest even deeper within Betty's heart.

Betty was thrilled the first time she saw her name typed out in bold ink. It was in the St. Louis Herald, on the top right corner of the Society page, in an article about the Queen of Love and Beauty competition. Next to the article, a black and white image of Betty smiled coyly at the reader.

Betty West: is she the favorite of the fairy godmothers?
This socialite is the lady of Prince Charming's
dreams— acute, boojie, and charming.
This magical trio of attributes can't help but win out.

Maybe I do have a chance, Betty thought to herself, giddily.

Then, it began to happen more often. Soon, the headlines began to pit Betty and Jane against each other. The girls agreed not to let the newfound media attention ruin their friendship. Newspapers were silly, anyways... they saw how, many times, the headlines weren't even true.

Betty would be lying, however, if she told you she didn't think about the bold-typed words as she looked in the mirror or when she couldn't sleep.

Betty or Jane?
Who will win the Battle of the Bitch Pack?!

Both girls were beautiful, smart, and witty. Jane's charm was just more effortless, while Betty had to work at it. Especially apparent in the love-department, Jane had a gaggle of boys lined up and ready to date her... while Betty continued to struggle for attention.

Betty asked a childhood friend to escort her to the ball. Potsy was from an old-money political family. His grandfather was friends with Betty's grandfather. Betty met Potsy in tennis camp when they were small children.

Betty's parents invited Potsy's family over to Westmoreland Place for dinner a few times when the two were smaller. The families lost touch, but recently, Betty and Potsy reconnected at an event for young members of the club. Now, Betty felt a little lurch in her stomach anytime she knew he would be around.

On the night of the ball, St. Louis transformed itself into a magical, twinkling snow globe. The city streets had been newly equipped with tall, incandescent lights. The street lights twinkled brightly in the sky, in between the falling snowflakes. They shined brighter than any star or moon Betty had ever seen.

The ball highlighted an aggressively sophisticated atmosphere in St. Louis's young high society. Guests were hand-picked off a list of St. Louis's best families. It was a high-stakes environment and it was easy to feel inferior. Many girls couldn't afford to keep up.

Betty decided on a shimmering, slinky evening gown for the festivities. Potsy also looked sharp in a jet-black suit and tie. When the dancing concluded and the competition was about to begin, Potsy escorted Betty to the stage for the much anticipated crowning of the Queen of Love and Beauty.

The finalists were all young, gorgeous, and from St. Louis's wealthiest families. As she and Potsy walked on stage, arm in arm, Betty's gown reflected prisms of light onto the faces in the audience. Envious stares felt like they were burning a hole in the girl's forehead. Betty nervously adjusted her dress.

Finally, the president of the Junior League made his way to the stage. It was time for the big announcement.

Potsy grabbed Betty's hand.

"...and the winner of this year's Queen of Love and Beauty competition goes to," the announcer took a long pause, "Jane Johnson!"

Jane. JANE!

Betty clapped politely with the others on stage. Inside, however, she fumed.

Still, Jane's win was of little surprise to Betty... she was used to coming in as runner-up to Jane. Boys liked her best. Teachers liked her best. Judges liked her best.

This time was just more disappointing because Betty let herself think she had a chance.

Potsy told Betty he liked her best, though. A few weeks later, before she left for Fermata and he went off to New

Haven for college, Potsy and Betty shared an innocent first kiss in one of the many empty bedrooms of Betty's parent's mansion.

They sat cross-legged on a quilted comforter. Potsy grabbed Betty's hand and gazed straight through her eyes into her soul. After a few lingering moments, his eyes landed on her lips. His fingers traced her profile until he let his hand settle in. He cradled her cheek.

Betty was smitten.

Potsy sent love letters to Betty at Fermata that spring and the next fall. Mail came at meal times. The headmistress hand-delivered each letter or package in the dining hall. The girls loved getting mail; it made them feel important. Despite her growing excitement, Betty kept Potsy's identity a secret from the other girls.

Mystery adds to intrigue, you know. Betty had learned that intrigue was what made people stick around.

Mademoiselle Snakeships West,

The fall leaves at Yale are lovely.
Wish you were here to see them in person.
I was thinking about you last night
when I went skinny dipping in East Rock.
The water was freezing.
It reminded me of how my heart has been feeling,
since we last got together.
I cannot wait to see you.

Love, Potsy

Betty was eagerly anticipating the reputed Harvard-Yale weekend in New Haven. Potsy sent her a letter inviting her to Yale for the football game and parties. While Betty relished in the shock of the invitation, she couldn't help but notice Jane's animosity towards the situation.

Who could blame Jane, Angel? Potsy was handsome, intelligent, and an Ivy-league man.

Of course, Jane was jealous.

Betty remembered Potsy's sweet, parting words well. "Betty, you're my favorite."

But then again... she thought, *Yale men probably say many words to many girls.*

Whispered rumors could be heard around the dormitories at Fermata. Betty West had a Yale boy who wanted her to come visit him for the premier football weekend of the year!

"College boys are only interested in one thing," a classmate muttered. "I've always known that Betty girl had loose morals," another tisked.

Potsy was unable to have overnight guests in his dormitory, so he booked Betty a room at a small hotel off campus. She took the train to Branford. When Betty arrived, she stood on the platform and searched for Potsy's shiny, black Buick. He saw her first, honked his horn, and cranked down the window to wave his hand at her.

Then, he got out of the car. Betty came running towards him, hair undone, and peacoat fluttering open in the wind. They embraced. Potsy pulled her in, tightly.

This was the moment Betty had been waiting for.

"Potsy," she murmured, into his coat.

Potsy helped Betty get her bags into the Buick; then, they got in. The two chattered on about the weather, school, and their families. Time passed quickly on their ride to the New Haven Inn.

At the inn, Betty found Potsy had already checked in. He turned the key and the door to their room opened with a creak. Potsy threw Betty's bags on the King-sized, four-poster canopy bed. Betty quickly found a bottle of champagne sitting on the nightstand… chilling and ready to be popped.

"Come with me," Potsy whispered. He grabbed the bottle.

He took her up to the roof of the inn where he had set up a few chairs, a table, and two champagne flutes. Above the trees, Betty giggled as Potsy popped opened the bottle and the cork landed in a tree across the way. She gazed at him as he poured champagne into the small flutes… and then they both laughed as bubbling, golden foam spilled over the side. They sipped the bubbly as leaves fell from tall branches and created a fiery autumn carpet below.

Just one glass in and Betty already felt tipsy. She spent years constructing walls around her heart, but the champagne broke them down like they were made of cardboard. She shivered as the air took on a slight chill.

Potsy noticed. He took off his wool cardigan and draped it around her shoulders. The sweater was itchy, but warm. It made her feel safe. It made her feel wanted.

When Potsy looked deep into her eyes, Betty remembered why she loved him. Potsy saw her for her.

Betty loved feeling seen.

Downstairs, back in the hotel room following another glass of bubbly, their naked bodies pressed together under tangled sheets. Betty's consciousness hovered somewhere over her body, instead of inside of it, like she was merely an observer watching the events transpire from above.

They fell asleep, bodies sweaty and intertwined.

A penetrating glare from the early morning sun hit Betty in the face, waking her. She closed her eyes but willed herself not to fall back asleep, as she relished in the comfort of being nestled within Potsy's arms. Their bodies fit perfectly... pieces created to be puzzled together.

This is everything I've ever wanted, Betty thought, groggily.

Potsy finally woke. Betty had long since fallen back into a slumber, but was still nestled in his arms. The crisp autumn air breezed into the room. The bed's canopy dazzled Potsy as the wispy fabric twisted and danced around the room. He nuzzled Betty's face with his nose.

She woke, and they made love. Again.

Finally, the lovebirds had to leave their nest. It was game time. Betty put on her new baby-blue tweed which maintained her prep-school style and represented Potsy's school. She wore her favorite black t-strapped heels; then, struggled to keep up next to Potsy on Yale's cobblestone paths en route to the game.

Go Bulldogs!

At a pregame party with Potsy's friends, near the Yale Bowl, Betty had trouble reigning in her excitement. The girls asked her to help as they painted large letters onto pieces of cardboard. Potsy watched from afar as the girls giggled and mixed paints. They worked towards the perfect shade of Yale blue. Betty's letter was a 'V.'

"What will your signs read?" Potsy asked Betty, on the way to the game. None of the girls would tell him at the party.

"If I told you," Betty replied with a coy smile, "I'd have to kill you."

At the game, Potsy was excited to see the girls's final product, unveiled at halftime. Their masterpiece read:

HARVARD IS FOR VIRGINS

The next evening, at the Branford station, Betty tightened her fingers around the spare New Haven Inn room key in her pocket. She shared a passionate kiss with Potsy before she boarded the train, and began the journey back to South Carolina.

Months passed.

Betty and Potsy exchanged letters back and forth. They shared the most intimate details of their deepest thoughts. They discussed injustices they saw in the world and hoped for a better world for their kids.

Betty caught herself daydreaming about their future. She practiced writing her new name in her scrapbook under the cloak of darkness provided by the cold dorm.

Betty Stewart. Rebekah Stewart. Rebekah West Stewart.

It wasn't the most glamorous name, but it would have to do. She wrote to Potsy:

My dearest Potsy,

How do you know when you're in love?

Mademoiselle S

Betty waited for a response. Days passed. Weeks. Time passed at a snail's pace.

B—

I'll know it when I see it.

Potsy

CHAPTER 8

FAMOUS

"Athena always, always has a plan."
Rick Riordan

Have you ever experienced something so pleasing that the tiny hairs on your arms stand erect? Have you ever experienced something so harmonious, it sends a thrilling chill up and down your entire body?

This phenomenon has a name: frisson.

Times I have felt frisson, include: in the movie theatre, on a first date, when my crush's fingers brushed mine; at the top of a mountain, breathless after a difficult hike, taking in the view below; when I've read words so beautiful they resonate in a place buried deep within my soul.

My first full-body high happened the day I wrote my first big hit.

I didn't even have a record deal at the time; so of course, I had no way to know that it would even be heard by anyone else. I just knew that I loved the words.

When I played the song for the first time, it was like my guitar's strings radiated positive energy outwards. Good vibrations coursed through my body. Frisson overwhelmed me; my entire body was covered in goosebumps.

The song was called *Superstarr,* in homage to my favorite artists... the iconic country music duo, Kevin and Lizzie Starr. After the song was released, a critic wrote:

> *Superstarr is a timeless love song that emulates Shakespeare and some of the greatest love stories ever written.*

I was flattered by the review, but my song wasn't really about love. It was about a record deal, my future, and nostalgia. It was about the glittering opportunities I dreamt of.

Sure those opportunities masqueraded in my mind as love; but not the type of love I had ever experienced before.

While I was daydreaming and writing songs in class at Phroneis High, Torò and Dad met for burgers and a beer down the street at Netherworld Brewery. There, a scheme was hatched to take over the music industry.

Torò sought to create a record label where he was in control, where he called the shots. His father was a big-shot producer at Universal; Torò felt suffocated by his influence. Dad heard Torò's story and was eager to help with his plan through his business-acumen and financial backing.

Dad had one condition, however...

It was a Thursday afternoon. When mom picked me up after school, she took a detour from our usual route home. My heart began to race as she pulled into the parking lot at Universal Records.

"What are we doing here?" I asked her. Mom didn't answer right away.

My fingers began tapping a furious beat on my bare knee. I looked, nervously, down at my wrinkled white sundress.

"Mom…"

Moments passed.

Finally she replied, nonchalantly, "I think you have a meeting this afternoon."

A meeting?

I looked at her, eyes wide. Mom grinned.

We walked past a manicured hedge and into the front door, where a blonde secretary quickly ushered us down a hallway and into a plush room. Dad was sitting at a long conference table, waiting for us, across from a familiar man with a goatee... Torò.

Surprise!

Dad and Torò filled me in on everything... the meetings at Netherworld Brewery, the newly established Gemini Records, and most importantly, my record deal. With Gemini, I would be able to write my own music.

"Me and a few buddies just don't like the way things are run at Universal," Torò told me, "and I thought I could do things better myself. After a few good years in the stock market, I decided to quit my job at the studio and start a label on my own. We're going to take over the world, Kid."

Kid. I cringed, a little, internally. That wasn't the first time he called me *Kid*, and it would not be the last.

I was also taken aback by his animosity towards Universal Records... especially given the fact that our meeting took place in one of Universal's fancy meeting rooms. Still, I was impressed by Torò's confidence.

"You're like the special sauce, Kid... the secret ingredient," Torò told me with a sinister grin. "Together, we can take over the world!"

If confident Torò thought I could assist with his world domination efforts, that's what I wanted, too.

Looking back, I'm sure Torò expected our meeting to go quickly. He later told me that he had to cancel another meeting that he had scheduled after mine.

"It shouldn't take long," I can imagine Dad saying as Torò chowed on his double bacon cheeseburger. "We'll tell Rae our plan. She will be so excited, she'll just sign the contract. No questions."

To the men's surprise, I sat there and read each word of the 21-page document like it was my Last Will and Testament. Though I was young, I realized some cruel truths of the world. No one would look out for my best interest better than me.

I asked Torò questions. I asked Dad questions. I negotiated.

Mom read the contract. I paced the conference room. The men left for a coffee break.

"What do you think, Mom?" I asked, "Is this right for me?"

She wrapped her arms around me. "Rhea, Baby, I've always seen how bright that light within you shines. Now, it's time for the world to see it, too."

The Harmonía family and Gemini Records arrived at a deal. A silent electricity buzzed around the room, like the wind, as Torò handed me a heavy fountain pen.

I signed the contract, on the dotted line, with a swish.

Torò left the room to look for a secretary to take our picture. A few minutes later, a blonde woman with a camera followed him back in. She got our attention.

Torò stood behind me. Mom and Dad were to my right. "Say cheese," the secretary said. She clicked a snapshot.

The moment was preserved for eternity.

Instead of walking down the halls of Phroneis the next day, I floated. My mind was five-hundred miles away. A teacher could have told me the secret behind the mysteries of the Great Pyramids of Giza, and I still wouldn't have paid any attention.

I was consumed with thoughts about my record deal, but I couldn't tell people at school about it just yet. Except for Abbe. I told Abbe everything.

After school, she and I walked to the park to read near the Parthenon. While Abbe was lost in Narnia, I told Athena about my record deal. Under the goddess's 42-foot shadow, I felt aligned with the universe.

I think I'm on the right path, I remember thinking.

Maybe I was.

In the years to come, however, I frequently cursed Athena: *the goddess of wisdom, ha!*

If only she had warned me.

When I signed on the dotted line, I became a commodity. Rae Harmonía: the newest, shiniest product to be sold in a system that is compelled towards limitless growth.

Damn you, Athena, for not telling me this back then.

Blissfully unaware, exuberant... it felt like I had signed my name in the sky in gold ink. The world was my oyster. My possibilities were endless.

Gemini Records sent my song, *Superstarr*, to the radio as a single. Within a week, it reached number 13 on the Billboard top 100 chart. I released my first album... self titled, *Harmonía*. Within a month, it went platinum.

I deserve this, I thought. *I've done what I'm supposed to do. I work hard and am nice to people.*

But, I subscribed to an erroneous mindset.

Good things happen to good people; bad things happen to bad people, I thought. *My dreams are coming true; so, I must be one of the good ones.*

As my career grew, Mom's prophecy came true. The world around me began to see how bright my light shined.

Young girls stopped me on the street asking for my autograph. Out for lunch with Abbe, we'd spot paparazzi hiding in the bushes; their telescopic lenses pointed at our table like we were animals in the zoo.

I'd see the pictures later, on TMZ, and hate myself.

I wish I were prettier, I thought. *I wish I were skinnier.*

I look back and laugh at myself... what a poor, vain pop-star.

Onstage, performing, though; I was different... more confident. Onstage, I became Rae.

Rae was poised; she knew her worth. Rae negotiated her way into a great record deal, and her bank account grew by more zeros than she thought possible, overnight.

Sure, Rhea had great qualities, but Rae really shined.

Rae had hundreds of fans. She could entertain you for hours, or even days, on end.

Rhea only confided in her mom and her best friend. She never seemed to be able to connect to people for very long before something went wrong.

How could I, *the real me*, find harmony between the two?

I was a force in the world; maybe too big of a force. Newton whispered in my ear, his laws of nature reminding me to expect an equal and opposing one. Instead, I closed my eyes and stepped onto an even bigger stage.

Kevin and Lizzie Starr, America's reigning power couple and iconic country music duo, phoned me after my new song, *Superstarr*, hit #1.

Bored in math class, I had written the entire hit in just one period. The words spilled from my pen into the margins of my spiral bound notebook, next to drawings of right triangles and the Pythagorean theorem.

Superstarr was the story of Kevin and Lizzie's love. When I told them about my song-writing process, they laughed and laughed.

"You're a natural born star, Kid," Kevin told me. "...and you may be a certified genius."

Flattered by their compliments, my face reddened. I was thankful that they couldn't see me through the phone. I felt my hands tremble slightly. I opened my mouth to speak, but my brain was racing far beyond what my tongue was able to articulate.

I managed to stammer, "Thanks, uh, I-I learned from the best..."

Kevin and Lizzie Starr had an effortless, magical star-quality to them. When they started performing together, and Kevin proposed to Lizzie in front of a sold out crowd at Madison Square Garden, the entire country was cast under their spell. My parents were certainly not immune to their charm.

Dozens of ticket stubs, collected from Starr concerts which I attended with my parents, lined the bulletin board near my bed.

After I got my record deal, under the cover of night, I studied the Starr's old interviews and videos on YouTube. In my diary, I plotted the roadmap for my music career.

The Starrs inspired me; they gave me hope for my own future. I was fascinated by the way they met, the love they had for each other, and the way they melded their lives and careers together.

About a month had passed since our phone call, and I was surprised to see the name Lizzie Starr pop up on my iPhone's screen. Sitting in the passenger seat of Mom's Denali, my hands shook, yet again, as I swiped my finger across the screen and answered the call.

We exchanged the customary pleasantries. Lizzie then began excitedly explaining her and Kevin's summer plans which featured a cross-country stadium tour. As she spoke, I tapped my phone's screen turning on speakerphone. Lizzie's sweet country drawl filled Mom's car.

Lizzie went on, "Kevin and I want you to join us on our tour this summer as the opening act. Ever since you released *Superstarr*, our fans ask us to play it at every show. It's a crowd pleaser! We thought it would be the perfect closer for your set, and thought it might be fun to join you on stage for the song!"

My palms became sweaty, and my heart raced faster. "I'll have to think abo-" I started, stopping myself when I noticed my mom's head shaking up and down, vigorously, in the driver's seat. I paused. "Um, actually," I continued, "that sounds like an amazing experience. I-I'm in! Thank you so much for thinking of me for this opportunity."

My mom's smile emulated that of a Cheshire cat.

Thinking quickly, I added, "Of course, I need to talk to Gemini... and Torò; but, I think everyone will be excited to hear this news!"

I tapped the red button on my phone's screen ending the call. I turned to my mom, and looked at her incredulously.

"It's happening, Baby," she told me.

I could smell the sweet, sweet aroma of my dreams starting to come true.

When I was little, instead of playing 'family' or 'teacher' like the other little girls at my school, I pretended that I was performing in front of a stadium of screaming fans. I sang, strummed, and twirled around the fireplace. I could make anything my stage.

My parents met at a concert. Both avid music connoisseurs, they frequented concerts throughout my childhood. Sometimes, they brought my brother and I along for the show. When the weather was warm and if the show didn't end too late, we'd hang around in the grassy field afterwards trying to catch a glimpse of the performers as they entered their massive tour busses. I remember gazing up at the busses… speechless in their enormous shadow. When I looked up, I could barely see the top.

On the opening night of the Starr's Summer Show, my mom and I arrived at the Grand Ole Opry, five hours before showtime with our bags packed.

It was a Starr tradition to begin tours at home so, conveniently for me, the tour started in Nashville. A few days before the tour began, Kevin and Lizzie invited me for dinner at their sprawling modern farmhouse right outside of the city. They chattered excitedly about what to expect.

The Grand Ole Opry was much smaller than the other stadiums that we were booked. Kicking things off in a more intimate setting paradoxically helped ignite the spark for our massive tour. There was limited seating; the show sold out within minutes.

As the curtains opened, right before the giant spotlight blinded me, I saw 4,200 faces staring back at me. I flashed the crowd my signature, platinum smile.

"Hi Nashville, I'm Rae Harmonía," I started my spiel. "Thanks for joining us tonight! I'm so excited to perform for you. I'm only 17 and this is actually my first ever tour! It's great to start the Summer Starr tour right here in our hometown! Y'all are in for a treat,"

I broke out a country drawl, just like Lizzie had taught me. "Kevin and Lizzie have planned a terrific show for you. But first…" I trailed off, on cue, as my background music began to play from the speakers.

Sparklers went off on both sides of the stage which served a dual purpose of distracting and delighting the audience. I ran towards the rear of the stage and grabbed my guitar from a man wearing all black. Spinning around towards the audience, I managed to finagle the guitar strap over my head and pull the pick out of my pocket. Adjusting the small microphone taped onto my cheek, only slightly as to not disturb the adhesive... I was ready.

It's showtime!

After a successful show, I retired to my mobile abode. As a headliner, I got my own bus. It was equipped with two queen sized beds, an enormous living area, and surprisingly modern decor. My bus had a picture of Kevin and Lizzie plastered on the side; they loomed five-times bigger than life. The three of us took a picture next to their blown up bodies. Mom printed it out and hung the picture on the fridge in the bus's mini-kitchen.

From the gigantic windows of my tour bus, I watched our beautiful country whiz by: the flatlands of Indianapolis, Chicago, and Lincoln. The rocky terrain of Red Rocks, Salt Lake City, then Los Angeles.

The memory card on my camera, which my dad gifted me to document my journey, was filled with images of epic coastlines, mystical forests, scorching deserts, looming mountains, and sparkling cities.

America, the beautiful.

Touring was even better than I imagined as a little girl, twirling on her parent's fireplace. That little girl had figured out a way to make the world her stage.

Fans came out in full force for the Starr's tour. Hundreds of thousands of people watched as I shimmered and sang my little heart out, in different cities across the the country. I loved every minute of it.

Kevin and Lizzie disappeared between shows relocating to one of their many homes along the way, and I settled into my cozy mobile home.

The tech and lighting crews each had their own bus, a true rarity on such a tour. They had transformed one space into a party bus and the other into the 'chill space.'

The crew was older and wiser than me. They had been around the country a few times. We broke off into groups of four for Euchre tournaments… a card game that I had to watch a few times before understanding how to play. Some nights though, the crew would want to party. I had just turned 18, but partying was still out of my comfort zone. I'd retreat to my own tour bus, grab my journal, and write.

That summer, I became quite close with some of the tech crew, read 13 books, wrote a few songs, and spent a lot of time thrifting with Mom.

I also learned a valuable lesson: never underestimate the treasures you can find in a thrift store.

Still, it was lonely on the road. Touring isn't a life that is conducive to making friends or meeting boys. I hadn't had a date in a year.

My publicist tried to set me up with a few different guys, but that just felt manufactured. I always dreamt of a prince who would come and sweep me off my feet: of Romeo, throwing pebbles at my window.

It was late one night, long after I retired from an Euchre tournament, when my computer pinged with an email from my publicist.

Jimmy Stark was just cast to play James Dean

in the much anticipated remake of the 1955 classic,
Rebel Without a Cause. His publicist reached out.
I guess they are filming in Nashville this summer.
Jimmy would like to meet you. Are you interested?
Let me know, and I'll arrange something for when
you're in town.
-T

P.S. I did some research— he's cute.
You should give this a shot. It would be great
publicity with your new album coming out.

Jimmy Stark.

I knew him. His raw masculinity and chiseled jawline graced the silver screen for the first time last summer, and he immediately cast America under his spell. Jimmy's popularity in Hollywood rivaled only that of the character he was now playing— James Dean.

Many know of James Dean— a promising, young actor who perished in a tragic, fatal accident at the tender age of 23. His sudden, stratospheric rise was juxtaposed by an equally shocking and abrupt death.

The life and times of James Dean coincided with many cultural phenomena— the birth of the Hollywood teenager, the emergence of rock 'n' roll, and the materialization of much of the modern world as we know it today.

Hollywood had been searching for someone to take his place for 50 years.

That morning, when the tour bus stopped at a gas station, I ran inside to grab a Red Bull. In line to pay, I saw the latest *Inquiring* headline which screamed:

Jimmy Stark is what Hollywood has been waiting for!

Sure, the *Inquiring* was a stupid tabloid. But, maybe it was a sign. And sure, maybe I bought into the allure...

Maybe, Jimmy is what I have been waiting for, too.

When the tour finally broke for a week, my mom and I flew back to Nashville. I was most looking forward to some much needed rest and relaxation... and hopefully, a little James Dean charm.

My break was lovely. I spent time hanging out with Abbe, tanning at my parent's pool, and looking at condos to purchase in Nashville. Jimmy Stark and I made loose plans for Thursday night.

On Thursday, Jimmy called early and firmed our plans into dinner at The Palm, a swanky night club downtown Nashville.

When I picked up the phone, his voice sounded uncannily familiar. Abbe and I paid $12 a ticket to see his movie last summer, so this wasn't the first time I had heard his honey voice; but, it was the first time its sweetness had ever been directed at me.

Looking back, it's clear that Jimmy recommended The Palm for dinner because it was in the hotel he was staying at. He bought me a few lemon-drop martinis; they were some of the first cocktails I had ever tried. Jimmy ordered himself an Old Fashioned.

We drank. We laughed. It was an enjoyable evening. As we looked at our schedules for the next year, however, it seemed impossible that we could make things work.

Still, Jimmy bought me another drink. "Let's take it to-go," he said, smoothly.

I took a deep breath and stood up.

I'm not sure if it was his honey voice or the lemon-drops, but Jimmy had me in a trance. He grabbed our drinks; I followed him towards the elevator.

We rode it up to the fourth floor where he was staying.

"My room is right this way," he said, like honey.

He handed me the drinks, then fumbled in his pocket for his room key. When he found it and opened the door, I found a massive suite. I set the drinks on the table.

"This is a nice room," I giggled.

"You're a nice girl," he breathed.

America's Heartthrob, Jimmy Stark, was telling me exactly what I wanted to hear.

I remember his touch as he reached up to push the hair away from my eyes. I remember the frisson I felt when he looked down at my lips.

I licked mine.

Unfortunately, my dear reader, I have to tell you: *we kept it P.G.* Despite all of the rumors and stories that followed, I maintain: *all we did was kiss.*

It was a beautiful moment in time, though. For a while, I remembered it fondly...

Back on tour, for the last leg of the Starr Summer tour, I made the hard decision to leave Phroneis High instead of returning for my junior year. The label would hire me a tutor. I would get my G.E.D.

Fall came quickly. Back in Nashville after the tour, I made my first big purchase— a condo downtown. Mom and I spent a week decorating the condo with some of our best thrift store finds.

The tutor Gemini hired, a retired musician and math teacher, came to my condo for our lessons. Her name was Grace, which described her well. She was tall and lovely, graying slightly. Grace loved my apartment décor; she was a thrifter, too. I soon came to learn that we had quite a lot in common. I later came to realize the profound impact Grace would have on my life.

Grace preached an independent learning model. Under her instruction, I could take things at my own pace and learn the things that were most relevant to me. Looking back, I attribute my love of learning to her.

"Why do you like music?" Grace asked me on one of our first lessons.

I stopped in my tracks, stumped. I appreciated music before I could talk but couldn't define what it was about music that I liked.

"I like it because it sounds good," I started, with a nervous laugh, "and because you can tell stories with it."

Grace agreed. "Music is obviously aesthetically pleasing, but what I find most fascinating is its rich history... and its rich significance in history. Some of the greatest ancient thinkers— like Aristotle, Confucius, and Plato— thought music could be used to understand all sciences and arts."

"Weren't those guys philosophers or something?" I asked her, puzzling over their connection to music.

Grace laughed.

"I have a story for you," she started. "It's about another philosopher— Pythagoras."

"I've heard his name before..." I replied, unsure.

"Probably in math class. He was the mastermind behind the Pythagorean Theorem— the oldest and most famous theorem in all of mathematics. The Pythagorean Theorem has helped us understand a million things about the world." Grace continued, "Pythagoras seemed to think that math could be used to explain everything; he came to that conclusion through music, actually."

"Everything?" I asked my tutor, confused.

"Back in his day, philosophers were not just thinkers. They were also mathematicians, astronomers, writers, and sometimes artists," she continued. "The ancients believed that a combination of these foundational pillars could be the key to understanding the universe."

She then told me the story of Pythagoras:

Once upon a time, around 570 B.C., in Samos— a balmy Greek island, in the eastern Aegean Sea— lived a newly-married man named Mnesarchus. He had just gotten his pretty, little wife, Pythias, pregnant. One night, snuggled in bed next to Mnesarchus, pregnant Pythias had a dream.

In her dream, the child in her belly grew and grew. Finally, the baby grew so big, it ripped itself out of her. To Pythias's surprise, the child was not an infant, but fully grown — shimmering and golden.

When she awoke, Pythias was confused and scared. She tearfully told her husband of her dream, and he quickly developed a plan: Mnesarchus would go to the Oracle of Delphi, in quest of answers.

The Oracle of Delphi was a priestess who was able to receive information from the sun god, Apollo. Her temple, on a mountain-top in Delphi, was considered to be the center of the world.

Commoners and noblemen alike traveled from all over Greece and beyond to have questions about their future answered. The Oracle often answered cryptically, but her messages were well-utilized. She helped farmers decide when to plant seedlings and empires decide when to declare war.

After a long journey up the mountain, Mnesarchus finally arrived at the sacred spring in Delphi. He waited in line at the temple. Finally, Mnesarchus came upon the Oracle who was sitting in the middle of the temple on a tripod seat. Three candles surrounded the priestess as well as burning herbs. He told the Oracle about his wife's dream.

The Oracle was silent for a long moment.

Finally, she spoke. "Mnesarchus— your wife, Pythias, is pregnant with a child of the gods. This child's life will reveal more than your common person. He is a chosen one."

Mnesarchus returned to his wife, excited. Their child would be divine.

Sure enough, when Pythagoras was born, he was much bigger and more developed than normal infants. The child tore up his mother on the way out. She died a few days later from blood loss. Mnesarchus was devastated.

It was only after Pythias died, though, that Mnesarchus noticed the shining golden birthmark on Pythagoras's thigh. It was the shape of a star.

My divine child, Mnesarchus thought.

Tears welled in his eyes.

When Pythagoras was young, his father sent him east to study with the Egyptians and the Babylonians. In the East, he learned about astronomy, math, and music. As a teenager, he studied under Thales, the Ancient Greek wiseman. When Pythagoras turned 18, Thales wrote a letter to the boy's father.

Mnesarchus,
Your son, Pythagoras, is like no man I've ever met.
I have taught him all I can; he is in touch with higher forces.
Pythagoras is destined for greatness.
-Thales

Unfortunately, Mnesarchus never got the letter from Thales.

When Pythagoras returned to his beloved homeland, after his studies, he found Samos to have been taken over by a tyrannical ruler. The letter from Thales was intercepted by the tyrant who became beside himself with jealousy. The tyrant had Mnesarchus promptly executed.

When Pythagoras returned home, and was told about his father, he had no choice but to flee Samos in exile. With only a small bag of belongings, Pythagoras sailed to Croton in mainland Greece. Almost twenty years earlier, Mnesarchus had traveled through the same place, before Pythagoras was born, en route to Delphi.

Pythagoras was crushed by the murder of his father but was determined to make him proud. He set up shop in Croton.

Legend has it, Pythagoras was walking to the market when he stopped in front of a blacksmith's shop to listen to the pleasing, percussive sound of hammers banging away. He realized that some strikes sounded much higher than others.

Curious about the different tones he heard, Pythagoras entered the blacksmith's shop. He observed that the smithy used many different sized hammers.

When prodded about the different sizes, the smithy responded, "I use the big ones to make big things and the small ones to make small things; sometimes I use multiple hammers on the same thing. When I do this, my work becomes pleasing to the ear. I work day in, day out. Time passes quickly."

Intrigued and convinced there had to be some mathematical explanation behind the phenomena he was hearing, Pythagoras weighed the hammers. He realized that they were ratios of each other: one hammer was twice the weight of another one, a different hammer was two-thirds the size of the last. He determined that these quantifiable relationships were crucial to music— absolute intervals.

"Are we talking about the intervals between notes in a scale?" I asked my tutor, incredulously.

"We are, and while I love that story," Grace continued, "it can't be true. That's not how these ratios actually work. You see, Rhea, every time a story is re-told, details are abstracted… but if you can find a way to sort through the nonsense, you may find the true lesson."

She continued, “Music historians think that the true story had to do with lengths of string rather than different sized hammers.”

A string, exactly half the length of another, will play a pitch that is exactly an octave higher when struck or plucked. Split a string into thirds, and you raise the pitch an octave and a fifth. Split it into fourths, and you go even higher… well, you get the idea.

This concept is known as the harmonic series; it is a feature of physics. It affects sound waves and frequencies in ways we can see and hear and in ways we can’t. Pythagoras was the first to find that harmonious chords could be quantified by whole number ratios, where the ratios of dissonant chords were not whole numbers.

“The details aren’t important, though.” Grace told me. “This is what is: Pythagoras was the first to understand that music has an inherently mathematical quality to the way it is organized.”

My tutor continued, “You tune your piano using the mathematics that Pythagoras discovered over 2,500 years ago.”

The lessons I learned from Grace about Pythagoras and mathematics helped me create my next album. I released it a few months after the Starr tour. Within the first four weeks, it went platinum with a million copies sold. Paparazzi started following me everywhere. I couldn’t even walk to the Parthenon after school to talk to Athena.

My bank account still had more zeros than I knew what to do with. Dad, who recently quit his job at the stock brokerage to focus on managing his investment with the label, set me up with his 'finance guy.'

I met with the financial planner. I brought my notebook and took incomprehensible notes about stocks, bonds, retirement plans, and other investment options.

It was all Greek to me.

Despite the chaos, I came away from our meeting with a key takeaway. It would be a smart investment if I were to use a large portion of my assets to purchase real estate. This, of course, gave my family and I the added benefit of being able to enjoy my investments.

Young, successful, and wealthy, I felt empowered to pursue my passions, even with the things that scared me to death. I went back to work: shooting music videos, writing more music, going to appearances, and winning awards.

I was Cinderella. My carriage pulled up at eight in the morning.

I naively thought that I had all the time in the world.

CHAPTER 9

THE BITCH PACK

"It's never too late to be whoever you want to be."
F. Scott Fitzgerald

Miss Weeks continued, "The 1920's brought a flock of young people to cities all across America in search of excitement, booze, and sex. In St. Louis, Missouri, Betty and the Bitch Pack ruled the party scene.

They wore scandalously short skirts, had provocatively bobbed hair, and danced to the freshest jazz music. These girls could make or break any party. The word of the Bitch Pack was like the Social Bible; if they weren't enjoying themselves and wanted to go elsewhere, all of the young men (and fun) would follow.

Desperate to keep their customers entertained, the headlines of the local newspapers also followed. Betty was the Bitch Pack curveball and often ended up on the front page. She had an unparalleled streak of mischief.

At a friend's cotillion, Betty arrived from the sky. She climbed up to the roof; then slid into the party, like Santa. At a family party, after all of the adults had gone home, Betty did a strip tease on the dining room table in front of her cousins. She wore sneakers under her evening gown for her own coming out party!

At that same party, Betty and Jane waited until a guest's chauffeur took a break. Betty then hopped into the driver's seat of the shiny, candy-apple red Cadillac V-16. Jane slid into the passenger's seat. The two girls took a joyride through the nouveau-riche neighborhood. Their pinned curls came undone; their hair blasted behind them in the whipping wind.

The next weekend, Betty brought dog food instead of corned beef hash for weekend brunch at Jane's... and she didn't tell anyone about it until Jane had taken her first bite. A month later, for Halloween, Betty dressed as a french maid, inexplicably equipped with a toilet seat around her neck.

On Wednesdays, she and Jane volunteered at the Home for the Elderly and Infirmary where her nanny used to work. "It's time for tea and a dance with the inmates at the local loony bin!" Betty giggled, gleefully.

Jane knew where the line was drawn, but Betty had no limit. She was addicted to the recognition; she relished when her picture graced the front page.

Finally, Betty was getting some long-craved attention.

Their fathers, Allen and Mr. Johnson, delighted in the girls popularity. The girls, however, were conflicted; Jane, especially, scoffed at the world they ruled.

Then, Betty finally heard from Potsy.

They hadn't seen each other since the Harvard-Yale weekend. Potsy was in St. Louis for the summer and staying at his parent's house. Their letters had dissipated over the course of the year, but Betty still thought about him first thing in the morning and every night before she went to bed. If anything, Potsy's silence had made her heart grow fonder.

Betty was ecstatic to see him.

When they met, it was for a walk along the riverfront. When they walked, Betty hoped that Potsy would grab her hand. Betty was tempted to just grab his face and kiss him in front of all the strangers passing by.

He never did, though; neither did she.

They talked about school. "Things are great at Yale." Potsy said. "My buddy Byron just got drafted by the Pittsburg Pirates."

Betty shared with Potsy her summer plans. She intended to join her parents in Watch Hill. Potsy had an internship with his father in St. Louis. "I need to make the most of my summer," he told Betty.

The two young lovers sat on a bench looking out at the Mississippi. Betty scooted closer to him and hoped he would put his arm around her. After a few moments of uncomfortable silence, Potsy cleared his throat.

"You know how much I like you, Betty…" he started, "but I have to start thinking more about my future. If I want to be a Senator by the time I am thirty, I need to be with someone who is more serious... a *politician's wife,*" he emphasized. "Someone less like Clara Bow and more like Eleanor Roosevelt."

Betty stared at him, speechless, preoccupied with her attempt to swallow her tears down. She bit her tongue until she tasted blood.

"Um," Betty paused. "I understand…" she trailed off.

She said it more like a question, though, and was unable to muster anything more.

A few more silent, uncomfortable moments passed. Finally, Potsy cleared his throat. Again.

He kissed Betty on the cheek. “Stay well, Mademoiselle West. I shall always remember you fondly.”

It wasn’t until they parted, and Potsy was long gone, that she finally let the tears stream down her face. Betty loved Potsy; oh, she loved him. She thought to herself, forlornly: *most people aren’t even looking for love. Most people are looking for someone that fits in with what they’ve been told they want their life to look like.*

Maybe things would have turned out differently for Betty if Potsy wasn’t the one who got away, Angel… maybe the world would be different, if Potsy hadn’t been the one that got away.

Betty didn’t hear from Potsy for the rest of her life; but during the twenty three years he later spent as a justice on the U.S. Supreme Court, she saved every newspaper clipping.

While the Bitch Pack drowned away Betty’s heartbreak with Dom Pérignon, America was suffering a tragedy of its own— the Great Depression.

After the industrial revolution and rampant speculation of the rip roaring 20’s, much of the country’s wealth was in the hands of America’s ruling class. Allen and his friends were like Midas among men. “Anything we touch,” they whispered amongst themselves, “will see endless growth and provide limitless wealth.”

The Industrial Revolution brought much needed changes to technology; but it also poked holes in the fabric of

America's farm economy. In the pursuit of infinite opportunity, farmers began to overproduce.

Overproduction isn't sustainable, of course. We know that from earlier in our story, Angel. Many farmers, like Betty's grandfather a generation before, found themselves in a financial pickle.

The government passed the Smoot-Hawley Tariff Act in an attempt to encourage the industries of the United States and to protect American labor. Still, unemployment in St. Louis was over 30 percent. Hoosiervilles and Happy Villages popped up under every bridge.

Things had gotten desolate.

Betty heard a story about a young woman who had to leave her small children for a few days at a time at an orphanage, because she didn't have enough food for them. The woman knew how important nutritious food is for a growing baby. She and her older children would make do with their meager food stamp ration of rice and sugar... but her babies needed more.

The rationed rice was usually full of ants and other bugs. The older children would spread it out on a baking sheet and cook it; then, they'd sift the bugs out. The woman formed the rice and sugar into sweetened balls.

For months on end the family ate like this— with just one meal of rice and sugar in the afternoon. Some days they would go without even that. The young woman ate her rice before bed. She gave herself the smallest portion. If she ate earlier in the afternoon, hunger pangs kept her up all night.

See, my dear Angel, reality often falls short of the *American Dream*.

Many things have undermined the realization of that dream for most who live in the United States: the ferocious spread of settlers into Native American lands, slavery, the limitation of the vote to white males, and a long list of other injustices and challenges.

Betty and Jane recognized this, of course… but, they were deeply rooted in some of the best parts of capitalism; they were entrenched in the glamour.

What were the girls supposed to do?

Betty and Jane had been the best of friends for many years. They told each other everything.

Betty always found it easiest to make friends with people who are similar to her, and Jane's house was almost as big as Betty's. Both of their parents were able to afford the finest things.

A few of their girlfriends, however, dropped out of Fermata because their families could no longer pay the hefty tuition. As Betty's driver drove the girls to school, in the Duesenberg, for their last semester, they passed the homeless who were sheltering in large wooden shipping cartons and galvanized metal shacks. It was a jarring juxtaposition to the aggressively sophisticated atmosphere of Fermata.

At school, the girls wore tweeds in the daytime and slinky evening gowns at night. On the weekends, they would go out in the city, Augusta, at night. They'd drink for eight or ten hours at a time. Often, the girls wouldn't come home until the wee hours of the morning; then, they'd sleep the entire next day.

It never occurred to any of them that they were spoiled brats.

Still, Betty, began to tire of the partying scene. Her mischievous rendezvous began to get her in more trouble than they were worth. Despite being surrounded by a band of followers, she began to feel lonely at every party.

Betty asked herself, *what are we doing???*

Many of Betty's fellow Americans were asking themselves a similar question. The government had employed a variety of new initiatives across the country in response to the Great Depression. They hoped to provide employment opportunities and stimulate the economy.

One of the government initiatives was the construction of a magnificent, state-of-the-art theatre in St. Louis. The Municipal Auditorium opened its doors in 1934, and their first show was going to be a somewhat controversial choice—*Aida,* an epic 4-act opera which revolved around an ancient Egyptian love triangle.

Betty's family was staying in St. Louis for the summer that year, and she had tired of partying. When Betty saw the *Aida* flyers tacked around town, she knew exactly how she'd be spending her time.

WANTED:

Men and women, aged 18-30, for casting in AIDA

Betty always thought of herself as quite talented. A few days after auditions, however, the night before the cast list was to be posted on the front door of the auditorium, Betty couldn't sleep. She was nervous.

All I want is to get a part in this show, she thought to herself as she looked out the window and wished upon a star.

The next morning, a few moments after the Cast List was tacked onto the front door of the Municipal Auditorium, Betty arrived at the theatre. She pushed past the throngs of people to the front, scanned the list, and found her name.

Betty West.......................... *Amneris*

Ecstatic but nervous about her parent's reaction, she ultimately didn't even tell them she got a supporting role. The costumes were skimpy; the opera was different. She didn't think they'd like it.

Somehow, though, they found out.

Opening night, her mother and father were in the audience. After the show, Allen turned into an eggplant in the lobby. Her father screamed at her. "You were barely wearing any clothes, Betty! The entire display was disgusting!"

She was mortified.

Betty thought she had real talent, though. So did her fellow cast members. One night, a big Broadway director was in the audience; he thought so, too. After watching *Aida*, he asked Betty's dad to send her to New York. The director pleaded with Allen. "Your daughter would be an asset to my acting guild, Sir."

Betty's poor, self-absorbed father was furious. He thought that the 'Broadway guy' was just playing on his ego... in an attempt to get money out of the West family to finance his production. Allen forbid Betty from going to New York.

So, of course, that's where Betty wanted to go more than anything in the world.

Allen and Rebekah tried to distract their daughter. They booked their children a cruise to the Philippines. On the ship, bored, Betty resorted to her mischievous antics. When she was caught skinny dipping with another young man after-hours on the top deck's massive pool, Betty's brother began to take bets that his sister would get thrown off the ship.

A few days later, docked in port in the Philippines, a band played the Star Spangled Banner to welcome the ship to their island. At the moment the high note was hit, during *and the rockets red glare*, the conductor was hit in the face with a flying plate. Betty was the one who threw it.

The conductor collapsed, and the band stopped playing. The crowd of people went silent. Even the birds stopped chirping.

To make amends and to avoid an international incident, Betty and her brother were sent off the ship to apologize. Afterwards, Betty nor her brother were allowed back onboard.

They were sent by plane back to the United States.

Betty's brother was furious with her. He was never able to collect the winnings from his bets.

Looking back, I think Betty was still so mischievous because she still sought attention. You may understand then, Angel, why when she got back to St. Louis, she married the first boy who bought her dinner.

It wasn't just that Jane had gotten married… and most of their other girlfriends, too. Betty was bored. She was lonely. And she was still thinking of Potsy.

Betty met Charles Dickson Walsh Pierce at the St. Louis Athletic Club after she got back from the Philippines. He was handsome, enough— tall, with thick, dark hair. From the moment he told Betty his name, which she found devastatingly romantic, her interest was piqued. Charles was a few years older than her and a Yale man like Potsy.

Yale.

Betty often took out the key she stole from the New Haven Inn and reminisced about the magical weekend she spent with Potsy. Anytime she heard the word 'Yale,' a film reel began to play in her mind: of autumn leaves falling and a crisp breeze fluttering in through the open window; Potsy's hand twisting in the hair at the nape of her neck; the two of them cuddled close together under the bedsheets.

Potsy could have been the one. Instead, he broke her heart into a million pieces.

Betty still thought about him often. She wondered who he was seeing and what kind of adventures he was experiencing. Still, Betty knew she needed to focus her attention on the men at hand.

Charles Dickson Walsh Pierce courted her; he made her laugh, sometimes. He helped keep her life interesting. The two talked, non-stop, for hours. Both imagined a place where they could escape the problems of the world.

Maybe they could move to a little cabin somewhere— far away from Hoosiervilles, perfect best friends, and Charles's boring 9 to 5 job at his father's company.

Charles and Betty were the talk of the Athletic Club. Everyone had their own opinion regarding the longevity of their relationship.

Charles could be flighty and impractical, almost like Walter Mitty; he often came up with harebrained schemes. "How could a man like Charles ever handle the veracious and stubborn Betty West?" People at the club whispered. "Charles needs a simple girl… someone who is loyal. He needs a girl who will pop out adorable babies and have a delicious meal prepared by the time he gets home. He needs a girl who can host a damned good party once in a while."

Betty and Charles seemed to be an impossible match.

Betty hated to cook and had never been a very good host. She also made her dreams well-known at the club: Betty wanted to move to New York City more than anything in the world.

Jane and Jack Heminway, her best friend's new husband, were living out Betty's dream in Manhattan. The Heminways came from old money. Their family had lived in the city for generations. Jane found herself quickly acclimated into the New York high society scene.

As St. Louis began preparing for World War II, Betty and Charles enjoyed a fine weekend on the East Coast when they visited the Heminways in New York. The couple had fun, but Betty found Jack to be cold. Jane was also more stand-offish than Betty remembered.

Charles and Betty walked, hand in hand, along Broadway. He promised her that one day they'd move to New York, too.

Betty really did like Charles, Angel. Maybe she even loved him…

When he asked her to marry him, on the porch of her family's home in Watch Hill, she said, "Yes!" without hesitation. Her father was impressed by Charles's credentials: his Ivy League education, promising career, and of course, family's money. Finally, Allen approved of his daughter.

People at the club, however, did not approve. They thought Betty had an agenda.

"That girl thinks Charles is her ticket out of St. Louis," the women whispered with disgust.

Betty and Charles planned a small, quaint wedding. This was out of character for Betty; many speculated that she had hesitations about marrying him.

On her wedding day, Betty stood at the back of the church with her arm linked in her father's. Betty was dressed in silky white; her father was in a black tuxedo. Allen beamed at his friends and family in the pews.

As they began their descent down the aisle towards her groom, Betty's stomach dropped. Charles stood there waiting for her, with a goofy grin painted on his face. The moment their eyes met, Betty knew:

She had made a huge mistake.

But, after the wedding, life happened fast. Betty got pregnant almost immediately. Charles drove downtown each morning for work; his pregnant wife, once a mischievous debutante, transformed herself into Susie Homemaker.

Allen, the couple's son, was born first. He was named after Betty's father. A few years later came Terry Anne.

The newlyweds were wealthy. Just like her parents before her, Betty hired nannies who did most of the work raising the children. Betty kept busy dreaming about the day she could get out of St. Louis. Charles promised her, "Someday."

Betty quickly came to an awful realization: she did not enjoy motherhood. It made her feel trapped. All she wanted was to go to New York.

In New York, Betty thought, *my life can start.*

Her mind was so consumed with New York, that Betty began to tire of the other young women in St. Louis. Plus, the debutante crowd who once worshiped her had long found new masters. Bored, Betty asked Charles if she could get a job. He agreed.

Betty began work as a nurse's aide at Barnes Hospital. She didn't enjoy it much. Aide work was hard work; she had to change patients' diapers and meet all their needs.

Maybe I should quit, she thought.

It's not like they needed the money, anyways, Angel.

Later that month, Pearl Harbor was bombed, and the United States officially entered World War II. Charles enlisted in the army and Betty bowed out of Barnes. Then, Charles's promise finally came true.

Betty was going to get out of St. Louis.

She, the kids, and two nannies traveled around the country with Charles as he was stationed in Denver, Miami Beach, Washington D.C., and Dayton.

In Colorado, Betty was fascinated by the depth of the mountains. She marveled at how the sun's rays peeked through the mountain peaks and how the clouds created dancing shadows on the sidewalks.

In Florida, Betty spent her days tanning at the beach while the nannies helped the children build sand castles and jump over waves.

During the chilly, New England fall, the nannies took the children to the park, while Betty took up painting. Ten days in a row, she sat on a bench at the park and painted the Capitol. The fall foliage provided a vibrant background to juxtapose the ginormous, white building.

The family moved to Ohio in the winter and Betty picked up figure skating to pass the time. Skating also helped her trim up; Betty looked better than ever.

While she enjoyed seeing the country, Betty began to tire of moving so often.

"Please, Charles," she begged, "let's move to New York… or at least find a way for our family to have some stability." To appease his wife, Charles talked it over with his general. Finally, he was granted a permanent base— in St. Louis, Missouri.

Home, sweet, home.

This, however, was Betty's nightmare. Back in St. Louis, Betty rebelled. She began to resent her marriage; if she was being totally honest with herself, she also began to resent the entire family she created.

Maybe I'm not fit to be a mother, Betty wrote to Jane.

At the Athletic Club, Betty tried. She joined the other young mothers, the 'Stroller Pushers,' for afternoon walks with their children in tow. The children enjoyed play dates; the 'Stroller Pushers' enjoyed each other's company.

As soon as cocktail hour rolled around, however, Betty would find a nanny to take care of the kids. "She probably would have been better off without them," the 'Stroller Pushers' whispered amongst themselves.

Though she had officially transplanted to the East Coast and was no longer a fixture of St. Louis society, Jane was still the talk of the town. The local papers in St. Louis continued to report on Jane's antics in the bigger city. She and Betty continued to exchange letters, regularly.

Jane was living the life that Betty had always wanted. Betty dreamt of the parties Jane was attending in Manhattan and the bright city lights.

Life isn't fair, she thought to herself with sad resignation.

A few months later, though, Charles was honorably discharged from the army and Betty finally convinced him to move to New York.

Charles had always wanted to open a little photo studio. Betty knew she could use that to persuade him.

"Opportunities abound in that city, Charles, you know that. In New York, you can be whoever you want to be," she told him.

Finally, Betty's persuasion was successful; that's how the Dickson-Walsh-Pierces came to own a condo in Greenwich Village. Their new place was on Fifth Avenue, a few blocks away from Jane and Jack. The condo the Pierces purchased was much smaller than the Heminways, but it was still nice.

A proud, new New Yorker, Betty walked through a crowd and marveled at the hustle and bustle. Time ticked differently in New York. Betty could feel it in the air. Things certainly felt more exciting in New York than they ever had in St. Louis.

It was as if the winds of the city whispered, *Betty, we've been waiting for you.*

Soon after moving to New York, Betty and Charles's marriage began to deteriorate. Charles worked long nights at the studio; contrary to what Betty promised, his photography studio was not prosperous.

Betty, on the other hand, spent her nights out on the town with new, shiny friends. Betty's girlfriends started to spend more time at their Greenwich condo than Charles did. Charles eventually bought another apartment closer to his studio. He began to spend most of his time there.

Finally, Betty got a lawyer. She filed for divorce. After a long and stressful court case, Betty maintained custody of the kids, both nannies, the Greenwich condo, and half of the Dickson-Walsh-Pierce family fortune.

Thirty, single, and living in the greatest city in the world, Betty never felt more alive. She was bright, attractive, and engaging. Still, she lived on the fringes of a society she desperately wanted to fit into. She held a few jobs— a receptionist at an advertising firm, then a sales girl at a designer boutique. None stuck. It didn't matter.

She focused on her hobbies. She tried her hand at music composition but wasn't very good. Her friends teased her. She stood her ground for a while, but ultimately decided to focus her attention on what she was good at— socializing.

Betty and her friends were notorious for partying, smoking, cursing, and dressing scandalously. It was a thin line, but luckily, Betty knew the cardinal rule: the only real crime in New York high society was poverty.

She stayed out until three or four in the morning at the Casino in Central Park or at La Rue on East 58th. One night, Betty and her new friend, esteemed socialite, Babe Paley, wore disguises to ward off the paparazzi and got drinks under the flamingo umbrellas at El Morocco.

After her divorce from Charles, Betty successfully burrowed herself further into New York's society scene. Her new friendship with Babe launched Betty's meteor in the city. Betty garnered a reputation.

And here, my dear Angel, history repeats.

Betty felt like she had been transported back to high school... except now the city was her oyster, and Babe was her Jane. New York had far more attention to give Betty than South Carolina or St. Louis.

Betty was in heaven.

Her friend Babe was an editor for Vogue and was given exclusive access to the freshest designer items. She and Betty donned sleek tweeds, silky separates, and French heels to wear out on the town. They were always pictured wearing the newest trends.

Many were jealous of the girls... and who could blame them? What the envious didn't realize, Angel, is that Betty didn't have everything. She was still looking for happiness.

What is there to do when you have everything else?

One cool spring evening, Babe invited Betty to a party at the exclusive River Club— a private family lounge on the Upper East Side. The girls borrowed clothes from Vogue for the event.

Members of New York's most suave and sophisticated families, like the Vanderbilts and the Roosevelts, belonged to the River Club. At the party, Betty and Babe made themselves comfortable at a high-top. Handsome suitors flocked around the young socialites.

I'm lucky, Betty realized, *that I'm at a point in my life that people are still interested in getting to know me.*

She thought, *I need to manifest a partner who will bring me happiness.*

One of the handsome suitors at the River Club was a 30-year-old gentleman named John Archbold. He was tall, dark, and chiseled. He chatted with the girls for a few minutes. "Can I get you a cocktail, Beautiful?" John asked Betty, with a grin.

When he left, Babe squeezed Betty's waist and purred, "He comes from old-money, Darling."

Betty thought John was fine but just that... until he stuck around for awhile, and they got to talking. John thought Betty was irresistible, and he told her so. He told her all the things she wanted and needed to hear.

John told Betty the things that she really should have been told by her father, Angel.

Looking back, I think that may be why Betty always mistook attention for love... regardless, my dear, you'll never guess what happens next."

CHAPTER 10

HOLIDAY HOUSE

"You will have bad times... but they will always wake you up to the stuff you weren't paying attention to."
Robin Williams

New York, New York.

A city that never sleeps and where your wildest dreams can come true. If you can make it in New York City, you can make it virtually anywhere.

My enthusiasm to invest in real estate led to the purchase of a renovated brownstone apartment in a budding neighborhood… Tribeca. I was giddy with excitement; living in the greatest city on Earth.

I'm ready for my life to get started, I remember thinking.

Sometimes, I like to pause and think about which moments lead to others. It's pretty to think about life like it's destined... like, just maybe, you can find definable patterns that can help make sense of some of the chaos.

Looking back, it's clear that moving to New York City changed the trajectory of my life.

Remember that little girl from small-town Pennsylvania who spent so many afternoons after school in her twin-sized bed crying into her mother's arms? Well, in New York, that girl was crying in a penthouse apartment that overlooked the Hudson, in the trendy triangle below Canal Street.

Mom's words echoed in my mind: *the light inside of you shines brighter than the lights of New York City.*

Flashback to a few weeks earlier... the MTV Video Music Awards were coming up at Radio City Music Hall, and my publicist informed me that Jimmy Stark would be announcing the biggest award of the night: the VMA for Video of the Year. My music video for *Superstarr*, which Kevin, Lizzie, and I recorded on tour, secured me a nomination. MTV asked me to close out the show with a live performance of the smash hit.

Once upon a time, when I was sending out National Anthem demo tapes, I would have been over the moon to perform in front of 20,000 people. At the VMAs, 20 million eyes would be on me.

I was beside myself.

Video of the Year was one of the first big awards that I was nominated for. I was nervous and excited for the show—for the award, of course, and for my performance. But, I was maybe more flustered about seeing Jimmy. We hadn't talked much since that night at the Palms, still, I often thought about his James Dean charm.

The tabloids frequently storied us together. Some headlines were flattering; some weren't. Jimmy and I had ended on good terms, though... or so I thought.

I looked for Jimmy before the show started: on the red carpet, and then, in the auditorium. I couldn't find him anywhere. It wasn't until time came for the much anticipated Video of the Year Award that I finally got a glimpse of Jimmy's chiseled, Zeus-like body. It was on stage and making its way towards the microphone.

America took a deep, collective breath.

I forgot how beautiful Jimmy Stark is.

Onstage, Jimmy began to speak and I found myself transfixed; once again, I was lost in the sweetness. The rest of the audience was smitten alongside me. "There were many outstanding videos this year," Jimmy drawled, like honey. "Congratulations to all of the nominees..."

He trailed off as a film reel played on a big screen on stage: snippets of the nominees' videos. The Starrs and I were first up and larger than life… even larger than their faces on the side of the tour bus. Beyoncé's video flashed onto the screen next. Then, Lady Gaga's. A few more videos played; with each, I lost confidence in my own ability to win.

It's fine, I thought to myself. *Just get ready to perform.*

My first-ever, live-on-television performance of *Superstarr* was up next.

In my velvet padded theatre seat, I was shaking… so I took a few deep breaths. I closed my eyes and took a couple more.

Inhale. Exhale.

Inhale. Exhale.

My eyes fluttered open, and I noticed that a camera-guy had focused his recorder on my face. I faked a smile.

Finally, it was time.

Drum roll, please.

"...and," Jimmy boomed, "the VMA for Best Music Video goes to..." he paused, as he opened an envelope and took out the small piece of paper that was inside. He smirked; "*Superstarr* and Rae Harmonía!"

I won? I won!

My internal conversation was interrupted by a thunderous boom of applause. I covered my mouth in shock. Paralyzed.

Snap out of it, Rae!

I stood abruptly and hugged my mom. As I made my way towards the stage, Jimmy and I made eye contact, but it felt almost... awkward?

Things are only awkward if you make them awkward, Rae, I coached myself. When I got to the stage, Jimmy and I embraced. *I'm chill; this is normal.*

Still, Jimmy barely looked at me as he handed me the award. He stepped over to the side of the stage, where a few tech guys waited for the next scene change. When Jimmy got over there, I saw them laugh.

It's fine. This is normal.

I took another deep breath, turned to the crowd, and began to speak into the microphone. "MTV— thank you! I'm freaking out right now! I couldn't articulate how much this award means to a new artist like me... so I'm not even going to try! Instead, I have some people I'd like to thank..."

I shakily took out the list in my pocket— my fans, Mom, Dad, my brother, Torò, Abbe... the list went on. I smoothed the paper and cleared my throat.

It was at that exact moment when Jimmy (who apparently didn't remember that he was wearing a personal microphone) muttered to the tech guys, in his sweet as honey voice, "I can't believe that no-talent slut won."

His voice projected from the speakers and penetrated through me like a crystal clear dagger.

I can't believe that no-talent slut won.

The audience heard him, too, as did the millions of listeners watching from home. Some gasped; others laughed. As I stood there, alone in the spotlight, limply holding my award, I heard the roar of their laughter.

I froze, lost for words, mouth agape. I think I blacked out for a few seconds.

Oh my god, I thought, *they're all laughing at me.*

Oh Rae… what a poor, vain pop star.

Looking back, it's clear. That one little sentence changed the course of my destiny.

The rest of the night was a blur.

Someone ushered me from the stage, towards the back, to get ready for my performance. I was scheduled to perform *Superstarr* right after the announcement for Video of the Year. Somehow, I made it through my song.

Mom consoled me afterwards. "You did amazing, Baby. I couldn't even tell you were upset."

After the show, all of my interviews focused on the slut comment rather than my win or my performance. I choked, trying to explain.

"I'm not sure what Jimmy was talking about..." I told a reporter from the Inquiring. "We hung out when I was on break from the Starr tour in Nashville last summer but nothing happened. We haven't really talked since. I'm as confused as you are."

At the same time, Jimmy was doing interviews of his own. His story was different, though: *Rae and I met up a few times this summer in Nashville... and she was friendly. Too friendly, if you know what I mean.*

The morning after the VMA's, the front page of the Inquiring screamed:

Who do you believe?!
America's Heartthrob or its Most Promiscuous Pop-star?

People chose sides. It seemed as if everyone chose Jimmy's.

America's Sweetheart transformed into America's Most Promiscuous Pop-star in an instant. I denied the rumors, of course, but Rae Harmonía was still labeled a liar.

After the incident, I got so much hate mail sent to my P.O. Box that we had to remove the contact information from my website. The brick walls of my luxe New York apartment watched as I wilted with the shift of wind.

The walls watched on, as I packed for my first international stadium tour, brought home a few more Grammy awards, and then, started recording another album.

Life's funny like that.

From my favorite perch— a bay window bench, lined with overflowing bookcases— I heard the city singing. I sat with my eyes closed and listened. The buzz was one of the things I loved most about New York.

There were a million things I loved about New York, of course: the melted mozzarella dripping off a slice of pepperoni at Joe's, the twinkling lights seen from the observation deck at the top of the Rockefeller, and the smoky, chemically stabilized aroma of roasting hot dogs wafting through Central Park.

Nostalgia hits me as I look at some pictures on the wall in my Tribeca apartment. One is a Polaroid taken the day Abbe helped me move in… a month before the VMAs.

We left my bags, largely unpacked, on the weathered hardwood floor of my new apartment and drove to the Upper East Side to grab a bite to eat. We walked through the park; then, got lunch at Cosi to-go. The plan was to eat our salads on the steps of the Metropolitan Museum of Art. Abbe bought us plaid headbands for the momentous occasion.

The Met Steps were the #1 destination on our 'To-Do in NYC' list— written in Nashville at Di's Halloween Party, sophomore year. We dressed up as 'Gossip Girls,' from our favorite TV show: me as Serena van der Woodsen and Abbe as Blair Waldorf. Back then, we barely fit the part.

Now we sat on the Met steps; nibbling our salads, wearing our plaid headbands, and guarding oversized Louis Vuittons. My gift to her.

I asked Tom, my bodyguard, to snap a picture of us. Looking at it transports me back to a different lifetime; one in which Abbe and I were so young… so innocent.

After moving me into my New York apartment, Abbe moved west to the land of Hoosiers: Indianapolis, Indiana.

Butler University is a small, liberal arts school that is reputed for their top-notch academics and underdog basketball program. During Abbe's freshman year, the Butler Bulldogs went to the NCAA March Madness Championship game. They won at the buzzer in an epic Cinderella story. The Final Four took place at Madison Square Garden— a stone's throw from my Tribeca penthouse.

I booked Abbe a plane ticket from the Indianapolis International Airport to John F. Kennedy and bought us second row seats for the championship game. We went together, our faces painted Butler blue. In my Butler gear, I fit into the crowd. I was thrilled that nobody recognized me.

The basketball game was a nail-biter. The last minute was legendary.

There were three seconds left, and the Bulldogs trailed 59-60… but, Butler had the ball. A millisecond before the buzzer went off, #21, Butler's star player, launched a mid-court rocket.

The crowd went silent.

The basketball hit the rim and circled around for what felt like eternity. Everyone held their breath. Finally, the ball fell… into the basket.

#21 made it. Butler won the championship. We rushed the court. *Go Bulldogs!*

Abbe and I still talk about the thrill.

It's fun to juxtapose happy memories with the tragedies of my then-reality.

After the initial shock of the slut scandal wore off, I found myself struggling to manage the type of depression you spiral into when hundreds of people send you hate mail. Each 'pen-pal' relished in the opportunity to point out my flaws… like I didn't already see them myself.

Eventually, my publicist started sorting through my mail to save me the pain.

Somehow, I understood the inevitable tragedy of my Cinderella story. Life has ebbs and flows. When a story became a tragedy, I knew what to do.

I'm going to ignore it. I thought, *I'll write myself out of their narrative.*

Still, I'd be lying if I told you I didn't think about it under the covers late at night… the hate, the deceit, the shame.

"Let bygones be bygones, Kid," Toròtexted me.

I took a screenshot of his text and made it my screensaver. If I caught myself thinking, *everyone hates me,* I snapped my wrist with a hair band… kind of like electric shock therapy.

Every action has an equal and opposite one, I reminded myself. Newton's law lingered in my mind, always haunting me.

Luckily, I didn't have much time to worry. I buffed my platinum smile, and got back to work. It was showtime.

My old school district was trying to fund a new auditorium. This endeavor would cost the taxpayers some ghastly sum and they were not happy about it. A group of community members was trying to block the construction of the auditorium completely.

The school board asked Mom if I would perform for a charity concert. They thought my meteor could make some money for the district in order to reduce the taxpayers' burden and, hopefully, the opposition. I flew back to Pennsylvania and spent the night at my family's Christmas tree farm.

Home, sweet, home.

“Testing, testing, 1 - 2 - uh, 3,” I said; a glare from the linoleum blinded me as the tech guys messed around with a spotlight from the back of my middle school’s cafeteria. Sound check was soon cut short. It was almost time to meet some fans.

I scurried towards the back of the cafeteria, near my crew. My ‘dressing room’ was back there— a large utility closet where they had set up a mirror, some lights, and a bowl of Sour Patch Kids. My favorite snack.

At the pre-show meet and greet, the hometown crowd came out in full force.

Remember Morgan and Jennifer? My grade-school bullies. They were fifth in line; apparently, they had gotten to the school before the sun came up. They both wore t-shirts with my face on it.

Morgan wanted a picture… Jennifer did too. Both also brought a couple of CDs for me to sign.

At first, I was flabbergasted.

The actions of these girls had impacted who I am at what felt like a cellular level. They literally changed my story. Morgan made me feel I was like dirt. Jennifer made me feel like I didn’t exist.

Now, my bullies were my biggest fans.

Maybe, I thought, *these girls don’t remember being mean to me.*

For a brief moment, I considered laughing in their faces. I imagined pushing Morgan down, so that her knee might get scraped and her uniform might get all muddy. I pictured myself pretending that Jennifer wasn’t there: making her feel like the ghost.

Then I realized... my reality is not their reality. They were living in a completely different story. It was at that moment when my own story started to shift. I started to question my own reality.

If a tree falls in a forest with no one around to hear it, does it make a sound?

If my bullies don't remember bullying me, did it even happen?

It did happen. My memories are proof.

But are they, really?

Memories aren't evidence. Memory is not fool-proof. How can I trust that I'm even recalling things the right way?

I can look into my journal and see the stories I wrote down. I can listen to my songs...

My music.

If I hadn't come home from school so miserable every day, maybe I wouldn't have had the inspiration to start writing songs.

Maybe, I thought, *I need to thank my bullies.*

So I signed their CDs and I did just that.

As the curtains opened on the makeshift cafeteria stage and the lights came up, reality became clear. I could have pushed Morgan down... but, the only thing muddy would be my face on her t-shirt.

I flashed my platinum smile at the audience.

"Hey y'all, I'm Rae Harmonía!" My spiel was like clockwork. "I really appreciate each one of you for coming out today!"

I put my own internal drama aside ready to lay some *philosophy of music* on their asses.

"It was really important for me to come out today and support the school board's proposal for a new auditorium. A space like the one they are planning makes kids like me believe we can be anyone we want to be."

I continued, "The creative arts are imperative to the foundational well-being of our society. One of history's greatest philosophers, Plato, is quoted: *I would give the children music, physics, and philosophy— but most importantly, music; for the patterns in music are the keys to all learning.*"

"The patterns in music are the key to learning," I repeated.

"I continue to be amazed at the ways I can use music to learn and create, in all areas." I felt obligated to add, "...including business."

That night, I was back in my childhood room, snuggled in the same bed I spent so much time in after school crying. I got out my notebook and did what I should have done in the first place. I looked into myself.

Except, I didn't know exactly who I was...

I started writing on the top of an unlined page:

Who am I?

I underlined the words with a bold swish.

I am a Grammy-winning songwriter. I am a high-energy performer that can sell out arenas. I am a thoughtful friend and dutiful daughter. I am a kind person and smart business-woman.

I am a learner. I am creative. I am a dreamer.

But those things were still just reflections of me, not who I am at my very core.

My reflection changed, ever so slightly, with each change of light. I was the subject of my own creation but also the creation of others. My persona was like a chameleon; its color and shape ever-changing, based on the environment around me.

Like a mirrorball, I reflect whatever I think the people around me want to see. Others see a girl who glistens and glimmers, but she's often just a shooting star in the stories around her.

I don't know who I really am.

I did know what I was anchored to, though: my music.

As I created my new album, *13*, I also promoted myself across the city. Charity galas, political functions, ribbon cuttings; you name it, I was there. My coming of age made me a novelty; I knew this. My light was what attracted others to me.

People are attracted to things that shine, I thought.

So are the headlines.

Trying to let go of distractions, I let myself fall in love. This time, it was with a city. Ironically, it was with the same city in which my heart had crumbled.

My critics say I only write songs about boys? I thought, *I'll write about moving to the most beautiful city in the world.*

The headlines are calling me a slut? I thought, *Alright, I'll focus my efforts on creating a group of bad-ass girlfriends.*

To make friends in New York, though, I needed to shine. I needed to emulate the girl on stage… I needed to *become* Rae.

In a city like NYC, it's not enough to just shine externally. Luckily, I had a few attributes that gave me a leg-up on the other 20-somethings in Manhattan: my travels, contact list, success, and of course, blinding fame. It wasn't long before my text log included the main actress of my favorite TV show, super-models I met backstage at Fashion Week, royalty, heiresses, Drake… the list could go on. I met everyone that anyone considered 'worth knowing.'

I collected friends like stones. I took care to dust them regularly.

Some of the stones were precious jewels. With those, I developed a closer friendship. When I let someone get really close, it was almost like they became a part of me. With a select few, it felt like we were practically the same person. They knew the glamour and the fame in a way that nobody else could relate to.

Sometimes, though, tragedy would strike. A stone might fall and shatter into a million pieces. Each broken stone hurt like it shattered my heart.

Despite all my new friendships, Abbe was still my best friend. Congenial, spirited Abbe. She was always included. My new friends all loved her. Still, I knew Abbe felt insecure around all these sparkly, famous people.

My new friends were frequently on the covers of *Vogue* and *The New Yorker*. They were gorgeous and confident. I began to realize that I feed off their beauty; as if somehow, having beautiful friends made me more beautiful… made me more likable.

Clearly insecure myself, I still tried to boost Abbe's confidence. "Please, Girl… you are just as amazing as any of them. Plus, you're my best friend." I reassured her, "They need to worry about you liking them."

My powerful girl army established official headquarters across the Hudson, in Watch Hill, Rhode Island. I had just purchased a massive home on the highest bluff… in cash. Holiday House. It cost a small chunk of change[7], but the purchase did make me feel better about myself after the slut scandal.

I also liked that it had private beach-front access. I hadn't been able to go to the beach for a few years… I had gotten too famous.

The album I released after the Starr tour eventually went multi-platinum. No remorse was felt when I used some of my earnings for the 'cottage.' It had two elevators, eight guest-suites, a pool, and private beachfront access. From the jacuzzi, located on the Master balcony, you could see the Statue of Liberty.

God bless, America.

Mom and I spent the winter redecorating Holiday House with some of our best thrift store finds. The house had been on the market for ages… its interior was stuck in the 1960's. My realtor, a sharply-dressed, gay man in his fifties, told me about the woman who used to own the house.

---

7 $21 million, but baby who's counting?

Apparently, she was the crazy-rich heiress of the Standard Oil[8] fortune.

"It is a tragic story," he started, dramatically. "The woman died… young, rich, and alone. And her kids! Oh, their story is even more tragic! Anyways, before Rebekah died," my realtor gossiped, "she hosted dinner parties with the likes of Elizabeth Taylor and Richard Burton, the yogi B.K.S. Iyengar, and the surreal artist Salvador Dalí and his wife… some of the world's best and brightest congregated in this very room!"

That spring, the girls and I giggled in the hot tub of Holiday House as we poured over the biography about Rebekah Harkness written just after she passed away from cancer. I learned the juiciest details of Rebekah's life; my friends and I marveled over the coincidences between her and me. She was rich and fabulous, but the headlines haunted her. Then, Rebekah let tragedy overtake her life.

Glad we have history to learn from, I thought.

By the dawn of July's hot summer sun, word of the Rhode Island charm and models swimming in champagne had flown through the upper echelon of New York City. Just an hour drive from Manhattan, Holiday House's eight guest suites were filled every weekend. My brother, Abbe, and a few of my new girlfriends were such frequent guests that

---

[8] Standard Oil was an American company established in 1870 by John D. Rockefeller and Henry Flagler. It was long-known as the first and largest multinational corporation, until 1911 when the U.S. Supreme Court ruled that Standard Oil was an illegal monopoly.

they had their own suite. I made sure to equip their rooms with their favorite snacks, beverages, and toiletries.

"Rae," a model named Keke giggled; "you are the best hostess in the entire world!"

I glowed in their attention. The rest of the world may have turned on me; but for the first time, it felt like I belonged in a group of my peers. Not only were these girls my peers, but they were also people I admired. They were pretty, invigorating, and interesting. They were people I tried to emulate. Plus, they weren't worried about the headlines.

Finally, I've found people who like me, for me, I thought.

I was young, successful, and rich. Holiday House was my castle. The world was my oyster. With my new album, *13,* I was going to tell my story… the way I wanted.

When the critics reviewed my previous album, I learned a new word. Transcendent[9]. After my first Grammy-winning album release, the critics wrote in Rolling Stone:

Rae Harmonia's song-writing is transcendental…
in a way that emulates the Beatles.

After the slut scandal, it became crucial for me to create a record that could tell my own story in a way that would *transcend* above the tabloid headlines and fake news. With *13,* I wanted to create the type of album that could be played on the radio 20 years from now. I wanted to capture the

---

[9] Transcendent (adjective): beyond or above the range of normal, physical human experience; not subject to the limitations of the material universe.

essence of who I was in a period of time that's gone but that never goes out of style.

After getting my G.E.D. in Nashville, I kept Grace on retainer to help me with my creative process. Searching for answers, I turned to her. I flew to Nashville to meet her for coffee.

"Transcendence," Grace began, "is that mystical quality that musicians have strived for throughout the ages. A piece of music that is timeless sits outside of time, beyond time, and above time. It is unaffected by time, unchanged by time, and the qualities that make it good last eternally."

She continued, "But, in my opinion, music, in and of itself, is timeless. Music is not something that just happen in the air; it is something that happens, first and last, within in the soul. How the piece of music was written is less important than the fact it was written. Still, that it was written is less important than the why."

"Transcendence can become almost a divine quality."

Grace trailed off and took a sip of her latte.

"You probably remember Pythagoras from when we studied Music Theory in Nashville," she continued. "He is often referred to as the 'Father of Numbers,' but I like to think of him as the 'Father of Harmony.'"

Grace continued, "Now, it's true: Pythagoras was a pioneer. He found ways to gather objective mathematical measurements on things previously thought impossible: for example, physical quantities, like sound. He was able to numerically quantify harmonic relationships. He attempted, for the first time in history, to logically explain why music is harmonious or aesthetically pleasing to our ears."

Grace told me that Pythagoras discovered that the most harmonious chords are created by the simple numerical ratio of the first four natural numbers which derive respectively from the relations of string lengths: the octave (1/2), the fifth (2/3), and the fourth (3/4). The sum of these numbers: 1 + 2 + 3 + 4 = 10.

Ten for Pythagoras was a perfect number because it contained the whole essential nature of numbers... it comprised of everything in the cosmos: unity, duality, and harmony. It contained everything needed to build a universe.

It was the tetactrys.

Pythagoras thought the entire cosmos could be woven into a grand design that could be perceived and understood by a gifted few. According to legend, Pythagoras could hear things that no one else could, like melodic tones that came from each planet. These tones formed a perfect and transcendent Harmony of the Spheres.

For thousands of years, of course, that seemed silly. There's a well known adage, and the plot of countless horror films: *in space, no one can hear you scream*. There's no way Pythagoras could have heard what he said he did.

"But you know what?" Grace continued, "A few years ago, NASA scientists proved Pythagoras right. They measured electromagnetic waves coming from the different objects in our solar system. Some Einstein had the idea to turn the waves into acoustic frequencies; then, he played the sounds on the radio. That was the day NASA discovered that the frequencies of the planets do make a beautiful Harmony of the Spheres... exactly as Pythagoras described."

Grace took another sip of her latte. I gazed at her, soaking all of this information in.

"Pythagoras was the first to prove that music, like mathematics, can be found everywhere— with no bounds to space or time. Music, like mathematics, is a universal code. It's transcendent."

Grace continued, "But, Rhea, much of his work is shrouded in mystery and myth. Pythagoras transmitted his knowledge symbolically: often in short, cryptic statements or riddles. He used few words, but those used were pregnant with multiple levels of interpretation." She paused.

"Kind of like poetry?" I asked my tutor.

"Exactly like poetry," Grace replied. "Pythagoras was like the great poet of life. He found poetry in everything— most importantly, in numbers. Pythagoras was obsessed with numbers. He thought they were mystically, spiritually, and philosophically significant. He supposed their elements to be the elements of all things."

Grace cleared her throat.

My tutor looked at her watch. It was getting late. "But we'll save that for another time...

"It is crucial to remember," she continued, "over the years, Pythagoras's life— like the lives of many of history's greatest poets— has been transformed into folklore. We must take stories about him with a grain of salt."

How relatable, I remember thinking.

CHAPTER 11

AN AMERICAN DYNASTY

"Rebekah rode up on the afternoon train... it was sunny. Her saltbox house on the coast took her mind off St. Louis. Bill was the heir to the Standard Oil name, and money... and the town said, "How did a middle class divorcee do it?"

Taylor Swift

Miss Weeks continued, setting the scene:

"Midtown Manhattan, 1946. Betty and the children raced down 26th Street and into a stale-air, urine-soaked railway terminal. Following close behind, juggling multiple large pieces of luggage, were two nannies. One nanny was young, dark, and slender; the other was older, lighter complexion, and heavier-set.

The group was running late.

Betty was hungover. She stayed up far too late the night before, drinking cocktails with John, Jane, and Jack at the Heminways. The children stayed home, of course, with the nannies.

Their soirée was a going-away party, of sorts… a summer farewell. Jane and Jack Heminway were summering in the Hamptons. John Archbold was sailing off to his parent's vacation home in Bar Harbor, Maine.

Betty, the children, and the nannies rushed past the homeless camped outside Grand Central Station, to catch a train to Waverly, Rhode Island. They were spending the summer at the West family's home in Watch Hill.

When Betty first moved to New York, back when she was still married to Charles, her old friend Jane had acted distant. When she and Charles got divorced, Jane had disappeared almost completely.

It was a cold, dark winter for Betty West. Sure, she had new, shiny friends… but without a husband or best friend, she never had felt more lonely.

In the spring, though, life seemed refreshed. When Betty and Babe landed on the front page of the *Inquiring*, and Betty began running around with John Archbold, Betty and Jane's relationship began to rekindle in a parallel manner.

Jane was jealous of her old friend. Betty's new friend, primo-socialite Babe Paley, was New York royalty. Betty's new beau, John Archbold, was from an esteemed, old-money family. Jane's jealousy piqued her interest in Betty again.

Betty relished in Jane's renewed attention. It had hurt her feelings when Jane drifted away. Betty stayed up, tossing and turning late at night, wondering what she did wrong.

Betty didn't realize it at the time, Angel... but, Jane's drifting wasn't personal. It was only now— that Betty was dating John— that she had the social status required to run in the same circles as the Heminways... in a way that even being Mrs. Charles Dickson Walsh Pierce never allowed.

See, Angel, John was an Archbold.

On their second date, John took Betty to Jersey. On the car ride home, John divulged the Archbold's story.

"My grandfather was a strong critic of John D. Rockefeller[10]," John started, "because Rockefeller's company, Standard Oil, began monopolizing the U.S. oil landscape. One day, however, Rockefeller invited my grandfather over for a cup of coffee... and then offered him a job. My grandfather took him up on his offer."

John continued, "Story goes: *my grandfather had a long and distinguished career at Standard Oil.* That's what my mother always says, at least. I think he retired as President of the company. Luckily he got out before the Hepburn Committee[11] started their investigations..."

---

[10] John D. Rockefeller (1839-1937) is considered the wealthiest American of all time and the richest person in modern history. He founded the Standard Oil Company in 1870, and controlled 90% of all oil in the U.S. at his peak. Rockefeller also founded University of Chicago, where the 44th President of the United States, Barrack Obama, received his education.

[11] The Hepburn Committee was created in 1879 to investigate the railroads' practice of giving rebates within the state. Prior to the committee's investigation, few knew the size and monopoly of Standard Oil's control and influence on unaffiliated oil and railroad companies.

Betty nodded, familiar. She had heard from her grandfather, Thomas, how the Hepburn Committee tarnished the reputation of some of his friends.

"I must say, John," Betty told him in a faux-British accent, "I'm impressed by your family's credentials."

The Archbolds were an essential thread in the fabrics of American history. Betty was star-struck.

My father would lose his mind if John D. Rockefeller showed up to our wedding, she thought to herself, with a giggle, as she stepped out from the terminal and onto the platform at Grand Central Station.

Betty shielded her eyes with her hand. Half a dozen locomotives stood on the tracks, like soldiers gleaming in the sun. She glanced around— looking for their train— but was really lost in her daydream.

Betty couldn't stop thinking about John Archbold.

She remembered their date to Jersey. In Atlantic City, John took Betty to the boardwalk. Betty took gleeful pleasure in John's broad frame, silhouetted against the setting sun. Giddy, like a child, Betty did cartwheels up and down the wooden planks.

John couldn't stop staring at her.

Betty stopped to gape up at the gigantic Ferris wheel; its eternal spinning hypnotized her.

Soon, John came from behind, and snapped Betty out of her daydream. He wrapped his arms around her. They felt like her favorite cardigan: warm, soft, and safe.

Betty relished in the feeling of their embrace. They stood there together for what felt like eternity. Then, he kissed her lightly on the cheek. When John pulled away, his lips brushed her collarbone, and Betty felt her heart flutter.

On the platform at Grand Central, a gust of crisp, early-June wind breezed by. Betty noticed tiny goosebumps prickling on her arms.

"Last call! New York to Waverly," the conductor, of a large locomotive nearby, boomed. His voice rose above the people milling about on the platform, and interrupted Betty's daydream.

All aboard!

As the train jostled along, en route to the coast, Betty sat in a train car by herself, furiously writing in her journal. When she and Charles started arguing, before the divorce, Betty began to journal more often. It was helpful to organize her thoughts on paper. During the stressful divorce hearings, writing helped her sort out her feelings and kept her sane.

Now, Betty knew that she needed time for herself to write and to think… so she booked the children and their nannies in a separate train car. Alone in her own car, Betty's journey to Rhode Island passed quickly.

At the Waverly Station— which was about a twenty minute drive from Watch Hill— Allen waited for his daughter and grandchildren. He saw the group coming around the bend, and honked the horn on his shiny Duesenburg.

Beep, beep!

The two children and nannies squeezed into the back seat, while Betty sat up front and chattered about her new friends in New York. She talked a mile a minute; Allen just stared at her. He hadn't seen his daughter since the divorce.

“I’m fine, Dad.” Betty reassured him, “You don’t have to worry about me.”

Allen’s eyes punctured a hole into her soul; Betty looked out the window and pretended not to notice.

Betty felt her mood lift as the Dussenburg sputtered down the rambling roads in Watch Hill and, finally, onto the bumpy, cobblestone driveway of the West’s familiar coastal cottage.

Why would I even want to summer with John in Maine? Betty thought to herself.

Watch Hill was home.

The quaint, seaside town spilled over with rich history. Betty had heard ghost stories set in Watch Hill, from earlier than the Revolutionary War. Her father told her that their neighbors, a few doors down, were direct descendants of Mayflower pilgrims.

Betty vibrated at the same frequency as the historic coastal settlement. Watch Hill had been one, positive constant in her life... it centered her equilibrium. The vast, inky ocean, which could be seen from anywhere in the town, helped her mind feel balanced.

That June, Betty enjoyed long walks down winding roads with the nannies and children following close behind. She admired the huge Tudor and Georgian homes which were surrounded by large pines and expansive gables. She marveled in the views of the epic Atlantic coastline.

Alone, Betty walked to the Watch Hill Beach at dusk. She sat on the sea wall and admired the cotton candy wisps in the sherbet sky. The boats in the marina became silhouettes against the vanishing sun.

Over Betty's head, seagulls flew: one by one, in twos, and threes. They soared back and forth over the Watch Hill lighthouse, without moving their wings. Gliding. The gulls breathed deep the sweet, sea air.

Something in Rhode Island's permeating salty breeze helped Betty forget about the perilous New York social ladder... and the shame of being a 30-year-old divorcee. The sound of waves breaking against the rocks below soothed her into a sense of serenity and security.

Sitting on the sea wall, feeling a bit like Humpty Dumpty, Betty set her intentions:

The world is my oyster. This will be my best year yet.

During the month of June, Betty settled into her family's quaint cottage with some books, the kids, and their nannies. The nannies kept the kids busy during the day, while Betty enjoyed the summer sun and salty ocean. She brought her journal everywhere and she often thought about John.

John.

John was a sailor. The Archbold men were master yachters. That summer, when John wasn't with his father on the sea, he visited Betty in Watch Hill. John was in Rhode Island every other weekend that June.

When he was away, John sent Betty love notes. Out on the sea, he scribbled sweet-nothings on a country-club napkin or bit piece of fish paper. At port, he'd send them to Betty—first class.

Betty loved to imagine John out on the sea thinking about her. As Betty sat on the sea wall and gazed out at the vast Atlantic, she thought of John, too. Her eyelids fluttered shut. She marinated in the golden hour rays and the way John made her feel: secure, wanted, and important.

You have to understand, Angel, Betty's divorce from Charles was taxing. Her subsequent splash into New York's high society was stressful. Still, Betty was far more confident than she had been as a debutante in St. Louis.

Betty didn't need John to tell her she was wanted, but she surely enjoyed hearing it.

When John wasn't around, Betty kept herself busy. She beached the days away, and partied all night with the other young adults in Watch Hill… many of whom Betty had known since she was a small child.

The group had dinner parties, which were by invitation only. Even on weekdays, the events often turned into black tie affairs. Watch Hill's social order was rigorously maintained by the powers that be at the Watch Hill Club. The club's members were an in-bred, closely knit group that required just the right last name and family money to get in.

When John was in town, he fit right in. Betty's childhood friends were also impressed with the Archbold-Standard Oil connection. John D. Rockefeller was an American idol. No name brought up images of greater wealth.

As the July sun set, however, a mysterious new sailor blew into the harbor of the Watch Hill Club and wrecked all of Betty's plans. This young bachelor— with an even more impressive tie to Rockefeller— quickly became the most sought over man on the East Coast.

His name? William Harkness. Most people called him by his nickname: Bill.

The past summer, World War II had ended in explosive fashion. Bill, a 46-year-old decorated war vet, returned home from dropping two atomic bombs on Japan to find that his wife had a bomb to drop of her own… she was filing for divorce.

Bill was aghast. It was an unexpected blow... *nobody divorced a Harkness*.

Later that month, tragedy struck again when Bill's parents passed away in a tragic boating accident.

Bill was devastated. Overnight, a distant cousin— who he was now staying with in Watch Hill— became the closest family Bill had left.

It's a tragic story, of course. Just don't feel too badly for Bill, Angel.

When his parents died, Bill became *filthy* rich.

Bill's grandfather and great-uncle were two of the original five investors in the richest American company there has ever been: Standard Oil.

Bill hadn't just met John D. Rockefeller— the Harknesses and the Rockefellers were business partners. When Standard Oil went public, 10,000 shares of stock were issued. Of them, Rockefeller controlled 2,667; between Bill's grandfather and great-uncle, the Harkness family controlled the same amount.

When the men originally invested in Standard Oil, they couldn't have predicted the magnitude of the gold mine they sat on. Automobiles were not even accessible yet to the American public.

As the country discovered new uses for oil, Standard Oil grew rapidly. The value of the company's stock grew in parallel fashion: quickly, and exponentially.

In 1900, when Bill was born, the Harkness family's wealth was on the same level as the Rockefeller's. The Harkness name had become synonymous with luxury and philanthropy in the minds of the American people.

After seeing Bill from afar at the harbor, Betty overheard some older women gossiping about the Harkness family at the Watch Hill Club... and thought to herself, *John Archbold, who?*

I jest, Angel. Betty really did like John.

It was just that the Harkness family's prosperity was that of a different magnitude than the Archbold's. Harkness wealth inspired awe. The Harkness name stopped people in their tracks. The Harkness family was about as close as you could get to American royalty... they were one of the last great industrial dynasties.

When his parents died, Bill inherited a stock portfolio that was worth today's equivalent of a billion dollars. But he was also newly divorced, and now an orphan.

He was numb with grief.

To drown away his sorrows, Bill hosted massive parties aboard his yacht in the Watch Hill Harbor. Onboard, champagne flowed like water. Nobody ever got an official invitation; but somehow, everyone who was anyone was there. Betty, in her hottest Vogue steals, was a frequent guest aboard.

July quickly turned to August, and Betty watched as Bill metamorphosed from sunken widower into charismatic Watch Hill it-man.

Bill's transformation— and, of course, prestige— piqued Betty's interest… but she had John.

John still came to visit Watch Hill; though, less often as July wore on. He still wrote Betty love notes when he was out at sea. John Archbold made Betty feel like she was somebody's favorite person— a feeling she yearned for since Potsy.

Maybe Betty should have been content with that, Angel… but, she did have a Harkness in her harbor.

Betty couldn't help herself; she couldn't stay away. At Bill's parties, aboard his yacht, she was drawn to him like a magnet. They exchanged a few stolen stares, but Betty could never seem to catch a minute alone with him.

One night, on her evening walk to watch the sunset on the sea wall, Betty took the long route home. Her detour took her past the Watch Hill Harbor, where Bill's yacht was docked.

Each night for the following week, Betty took her new route home and hoped Bill might be sitting on the deck of his yacht, watching the sunset. She hoped that he might see her walking and invite her onboard.

Most nights, though, the boat was dark.

Finally, on a warm Tuesday evening, Betty got her chance. As she walked home in the twilight, she saw lights on in the Ardea. She squinted and saw a tall, dark figure on the boat's deck… sweeping? It had to be Bill.

It's now or never, Betty told herself.

She shouted upwards: "Hey! YOU!"

She waited. Finally, Bill's head poked over the side of the boat.

Betty grinned, and projected: "Well! If it isn't the mysterious son of a bitch everyone has been talking about! My name is Betty West. I hope you'll give me the absolute pleasure of making your acquaintance."

She curtsied, dramatically.

Bill peered down at Betty's crouched figure. He laughed and laughed. He laughed harder than he had laughed in an entire year. In that one moment, Bill felt happier than he had felt in any moment since before he left for the war.

When his laughter finally ceased, Bill called back at her in a dazzling tenor: "Betty West! It's a pleasure! My name is Bill Harkness. I think I've seen you here before..." He paused. "I just finished a glass of scotch downstairs. Would you like to join me for another? I cracked open a bottle of 50-year-old Macallan tonight. I'm having myself a celebration."

But, the way he said *celebration* didn't make Betty think there was anything happy about his night at all. She finally came out of her dramatic curtsy, and called back: "You're celebrating all by yourself?" She paused. "Maybe I should come up!"

Betty couldn't believe her luck.

She had partied on Bill's yacht a few times that summer, but never received a personal invitation aboard. The open bar was on the deck of the Ardea, so Betty had also never been down in the yacht's interior.

Inside the Ardea's luxurious living cabin for the first time, Betty looked around in awe. She admired the tan, leather sofas and rich mahogany furniture. Bill fiddled around at the bar.

"On the rocks?" He asked her, with a bottle of spirits in his hand.

Now, Angel… Betty wasn't the type of girl who typically drank scotch on the rocks, but this was no ordinary occasion.

"Sure! So, what are you celebrating tonight?" Betty giggled, flirtatiously.

"Well it's been almost an entire year since I got home from the war," Bill replied, "and about the same amount of time since I got served divorce papers. My wife began seeing some Hollywood hot-shot while I was overseas."

Betty looked at him. She didn't quite know how to respond.

Tipsy Bill didn't notice Betty's silence. Instead, he rambled on, "Then, the universe got me again… a month later. My parents were out at sea when a storm hit out of nowhere. Their boat capsized... both drowned. The worst part? I was supposed to be out there with them." Bill trailed off. He finished pouring the deep amber liquid into a short crystal glass, filled with ice.

Betty continued to stare at him, lost for words. Bill handed her the scotch glass.

He continued, "But, you know what Betty West? I don't want to talk about that tonight. Tonight is for celebrating… we're celebrating our new friendship."

Betty giggled, almost apprehensively.

"Cheers to that," she finally replied, as she raised her glass to meet his.

Clink.

As they sipped on their scotch, Betty told Bill her story. She told him of her divorce, of her struggles, and of feeling less-than. She didn't know if it was Bill's raw charm or the aged-scotch… but Betty's walls fell down for Bill just like they had for Potsy.

Bill listened to her talk. When she started to get emotional, he put his arm around her. Bill made Betty feel safe. He told her, "I know how lucky I am— how lucky we are — even to just be alive right now. But, despite the riches and glamour, life can be really hard. Sometimes it's difficult to see the purpose of it all."

Bill paused for a long moment.

Finally, he rasped, "Betty, you remind me of my mother. Her name was Edith. She was such a beautiful woman. I miss her so much." Tears caught at his throat.

"Whenever I cried as a child, she told me: *son, it is okay to cry. You are given your feelings for a reason. Each story is written by the universe. If you look hard enough, you can always find the why."*

He collapsed into a tan, leather chair. "But I have spent this past year searching," he wailed. "Why am I here? Why was I left here all alone? Why do I have to deal with all of this pain?"

Betty reached over and put her hand on his shoulder. "You don't have to deal with it alone," she comforted him, "You can tell me about it. I will be here for you."

He reached up, and covered her hand with his. Her words were exactly what Bill needed to hear. It was like Betty turned the knob of a faucet; stories came spilling out of Bill.

Bill talked for hours. He told Betty things that he had never told another soul... not even his ex-wife.

Betty shared the same. She told him things that she hadn't told anyone else, except Potsy... fucking Potsy, still always on her mind.

Sometimes Betty still thought about him. She wondered what kind of adventures he must be having.

She heard that Potsy had met his wife, an Eleanor Roosevelt-type, through an arranged marriage between social families.

How romantic, Betty thought, facetiously.

Later that night, after two more glasses of scotch, Betty and Bill made love. The next night, when Betty took her nightly detour, Bill was on the deck of the Ardea waiting for her.

They made love that night. Again.

Betty began to fall. Hard.

But at first, they had to be sneaky. Betty and Bill's clandestine meetings went undiscovered for many weeks... This was partially because Betty was still in a relationship with John, and the entire town knew it.

Lucky for Betty, the nannies were the only ones paying enough attention to be suspicious. They whispered amongst themselves... *do you think Betty's walks are taking longer than usual? Did Betty seem a little... flushed when she returned?*

Soon, Betty and Bill were 'getting together' almost every night. At the same time, Betty continued to receive love letters from John:

Aug 13, 1946

My dearest Betty,
At night, I look up and can see every star in the sky.
Sometimes, I think I see you up there...
a glittering spiral in the cosmos.
The stars makes me feel less lonely on this wide, open sea.
I'll be sailing to Watch Hill in two weeks.
I've been counting down the minutes.
Love, John

True to his word, John's boat pulled into the Watch Hill Harbor on the 27th day of August. The minute he stepped onto the familiar, sandy shore, John made a bee-line for the Watch Hill Club. There, he used the pay-phone to let Betty know he had arrived.

When Betty answered, she told him, "I actually booked you a room at the Watch Hill Inn..." Before he could say anything, she continued, "... and, I will meet you there later this evening." She made an excuse and hurried off the phone.

Betty's behavior on the phone and his Watch Hill Inn accommodations were surprising. Typically when John visited her for the weekend, he stayed at Betty's family's cottage.

Poor John was clueless of the heartbreak to come.

That afternoon, Betty plotted her breakup speech, while John was at the beach... lost in his daydream about a weekend in bed with his lover. That night, Betty crushed John's dreams when she told him they needed to break up.

"It's been tough for me, with you at sea," she told him… an excuse. Betty continued, "I've met someone else. I'm sorry."

John looked at her, bemused. At first, he thought she was just playing a prank.

My silly Betty, he thought.

But as she stared back at him with a blank face, a grim look of realization washed over his, clouding his All-American features.

Betty was not playing around.

Early the next morning, John Archbold sailed out of the Watch Hill Harbor... and rumor has it, he was so traumatized by the Betty West saga, that no Archbold ever visited that God-forsaken coastal town again.

With John out of the picture, Betty was untethered. She was now free to pursue her heart's desires. But Betty had a one track mind, Angel... all she could think about was Bill Harkness.

Betty felt it in her fingers and toes; she loved Bill just like she loved Potsy. Betty knew, though; this time she could not make the same mistakes.

Betty couldn't handle a Potsy-type heartbreak again.

A man like Bill needed a certain type of partner... a political wife. A docile, Aphrodite-type charmer who stood, mostly silent, behind her besuited and gray-templed husband. A caring mother who's primary goal was to raise a suitable heir to the Harkness name (and fortune).

As if she had a premonition, Betty knew: if she couldn't find a way to conform to that mold and become the perfect woman, her story would end in tragedy. Again.

Betty West loved Bill Harkness. And by a stroke of luck, it turned out that Bill Harkness loved Betty West too.

In the end, that was all that mattered.

It took some soul searching, but Betty finally understood what she needed to do: she matured overnight, she toned herself down. She spent more time with the children. She only drank if Bill didn't know about it.

Betty played her role perfectly. She transformed into exactly what Bill wanted her to be. Within a few months, Bill asked Betty to marry him.

Everyone was delighted. Especially Allen.

The couple wed in New York surrounded by a small crowd of family and friends. You know, Angel... it's a shame. Betty never did get the extravagant wedding of her dreams.

Once again, Allen walked his daughter down the aisle. This time, however, a billionaire stood waiting at the alter.

Still, I dont think Betty could have predicted the magnitude of change she would undergo as she transformed into Mrs. William Harkness.

When she tied herself to Bill, her story changed. Betty West became inextricably woven into the story of the *American Dream: Monopoly Edition.*

Spoiler alert: that version always ends in tragedy."

GRAMMY AWARDS
GRAMMY AWARDS

CHAPTER 12

THE LUCKY 1

"We have so little faith in the ebb and flow of life, love, and relationships. We insist on permanency, on duration, on continuity. The only continuity possible in life, as in love, is in growth, in fluidity, in freedom."
Anne Morrow Lindbergh

I was 21 years old with three multi-platinum albums under my belt. The past year at the Grammys, I swept… and became the youngest female to have been awarded my second Grammy for Album of the Year. *13* had launched me into a stratosphere that Mom called a 'household name.'

I was one of the lucky ones. I was on the top of the world. But, I soon realized the paradox: 'household names' don't have much control over their story.

I've always thrived off control. When I negotiated my record deal, I did so with the concept of control in mind. I was young, but I knew my worth. I wouldn't let myself get taken advantage of. I read each and every word of my contract. I thought I negotiated control over my career. I thought I knew what I was getting myself into.

I didn't have control, though... most of us never do.

It turned out that I was just a puppet.

Two years after the Jimmy Stark slut scandal, America's Most Promiscuous Pop-star hit the papers again. This time, the articles were packed full of 'evidence' from the ancient, *scandalous* charade… including photos of Jimmy and I from our night at the Palms: us drinking cocktails at the bar (and me, of course, underage); Jimmy carrying both of our drinks, me following him into the elevator; me, with my heels off, walking barefoot towards his hotel room; me, about to enter his room, making direct eye contact with the camera.

I vaguely remembered the sounds I heard right before we went into his room... the clicking. It sounded like a camera, but I didn't see anything out of the ordinary. Jimmy told me it was nothing.

"Don't worry about it, Baby," he said.

On the day the *Inquiring* released the photos, I slept in. As I slept, the internet read the article. When I woke, I had 99 unread text messages. When I turned on my (brand new) iPhone, a blaring, baby blue alert immediately popped up. #RaeHarmoniaisCancelled was trending on Twitter.

Confused, I went first to my text inbox. The first message was from Abbe… she had sent me a link. I clicked it, and was taken to an article on the *Inquiring's* website.

When I saw the pictures, I felt violated. The article was equipped with direct quotes from Jimmy, with intimate details from our night together— some true, some not. When I read them, my cheeks became enflamed.

On my iPhone, I exited my internet app and switched to Twitter. As I scrolled down the trending hashtag list, I saw that over a million people had tweeted about me. Almost all of their tweets included the word 'slut.' Most also included the word 'liar.'

I felt embarrassed... like the whole world was shaming me. I wanted to scream: *you don't understand! It wasn't what it looked like. They got the story all wrong! Again!*

Furious about the article and the photos, I decided to call Jimmy out on his misdeed. Hands shaking, I swiped my finger across my iPhone's screen until I had pulled up his contact information. I clicked call.

"Rae," Jimmy answered, almost immediately, in his sweet-as-honey voice. "I've been expecting your phone call."

"Why did you say those things in the article?" I barely got the words out; tears caught at my throat. "How did the *Inquiring* get those pictures?"

Jimmy was silent for a moment.

"I promise you, Baby— I did not say those things. I still feel terrible about what happened at the VMAs... my manager pushed me to do it. He said it would be good publicity, Baby. When the article came out, I was also confused. How did they get the photos and information from our night at The Palms? I had my publicist call the *Inquiring* to see who provided the pictures..."

He trailed off, then took a deep breath. I waited.

Finally, he said: "It was Torò, Rae. Torò sold the pictures to the magazine. Torò was the one who arranged for the article. Torò was the mastermind behind the VMA stunt."

Flabbergasted, I hung up with Jimmy and immediately called Torò. When he answered, I was so upset, I could barely get out any words.

"You know what, Kid? There's no such thing as bad publicity," he told me over the phone... over my sobs. "I was doing you a favor. You're getting older, you know. How else do you expect to sell albums?"

Toró! I screamed inside my head. *You know me better than this! You know how this would hurt. How could you do this to me?! How could you say that to me?!*

I had nothing to say. So, I hung up the phone.

Toró stabbed me in the back; his knife poked a giant hole. Like I was a balloon, I began to deflate. In the weeks that followed, almost all of my air leaked out.

#RaeHarmoniaisCancelled was the #1 trend on Twitter, worldwide, for a week. Do you know how many people need to tweet at you in order for that to happen? Millions of Tweeters 'cancelled' me. Millions called me a slut. Millions of people thought I was conniving. Millions had decided that I was not a good person.

There's no such thing as bad publicity? I thought, between my tears, *I have no control over my own narrative. I have no control over what people think about me.*

When I came to the realization that I had lost control... to the headlines, to Toró, and to public opinion, I felt the desperation swell deep in my bones.

To take back control, I made some decisions: I would be the only songwriter on my albums, and my tour for *13* would be bigger and more spectacular than any tours before. I would work on my vocals every day and continue to create multi-platinum records.

I would be what everyone said I couldn't be.

I would be what Toró clearly didn't think I could be.

The duality of life caused me to experience both the good and the bad. My social calendar was filled with New York's most exciting events, but I often felt lonely in the crowd. I had millions of fans, but an equal amount of haters.

I bought a beautiful beach house in Rhode Island... but on my favorite beach in Naples, I got mobbed by screaming fans. I floated higher than the Hancock... but the headlines delighted in tearing me down, in pursuit of the almighty dollar. Negative headlines sell papers, you know.

Life has its ebbs and flows. I understood that.

Newton's laws rule the universe and my life. I can use dissonance to make me stronger and use hardship to my advantage, I thought.

I was the lucky one. Sure, some of my lows were world altering... but I overcame them. I did what I was supposed to do: I worked hard, was nice to people, and made my dreams come true.

Then, I floated into the party in a whimsical horse-drawn carriage, dressed as Cinderella… as if intentionally taunting the universe:

Come and get me!

When you are young— especially young and successful— it's easy to think you have the world figured out. When my early albums were released, screaming fans lined up for hours just for a chance to meet me. New York City made me her welcome ambassador. A family who was basically American royalty invited me to spend the summer with them in Cape Cod.

The summer I became an adult, I bought a multi-million dollar beach home. In cash. My castle was perched on the highest residential property on the entire Eastern seaboard with direct beachfront access.

Dad loved to tell that to people.

I felt smart... like I was living the right way for a change. I was a good singer. I was a good person. I was a good entertainer. These things gave me value.

People liked me— hell, they loved me— until they didn't. Tragedy would inevitably strike.

I was living a life that other people dream of, but all of a sudden, the sparkling persona I had crafted wasn't good enough. It was like I was transplanted back to my middle school lunch table. Instead, now, I only wished I was a ghost.

I hid, in shame, as rumors flew across the world stage:

Rae Harmonía is a slut!

Rae Harmonía is cancelled!

Rae is a liar— you can't trust her!

I heard that Rae doesn't write her own songs... pathetic!

We don't like Rae and you shouldn't either. Here's why...

Maybe I was overexposed. Maybe the level of success I rose to made people uncomfortable. Maybe society doesn't like to see a woman reach that level of wealth.

Regardless, the noise was loud.

When I was younger, I thought that if I just had more money or was more successful, more people would like me.

But, I forgot a crucial, age-old adage: *mo' money, mo' problems*[12].

On the love front, it became impossible to sort through the clowns. I never could tell... who wanted to find their soul mate? Who just wanted a piece of America's Most Promiscuous Pop-star?

I tried to focus on my girl friends. Still, there were problems there— insecurity, trust-issues, jealously— which were exemplified by the media, who never left us alone.

The media— these tabloids and talk shows— had no rules. They were writing articles and saying things about me that had no basis in fact. At the checkout counter, I'd see a headline:

Rae is pregnant... again!?
The father? Word on the street:
Hollywood heartthrob, Jimmy Stark!

Their 'facts' were printed in bold ink... branding me with scarlet letters. Their 'facts' however, weren't even true. Sometimes the 'pictures of me' they printed weren't me at all.

Soon, the articles were not just about boys. They were about my friends, my songwriting... how skinny (or fat) I looked. They were about what designer I was wearing, how many houses I had, how expensive my properties were... and how it was all, just, far too much.

---

12 *Mo Money, Mo Problems* is a Grammy-nominated single by The Notorious B.I.G., released posthumously. It topped the Billboard charts for two weeks in 1997.

The headlines aren't true, I thought.

Most of them weren't true…

Are they true?

I had been talking to a therapist for a few months, on recommendation from Torò. I was apprehensive at first, but he chided me: "Kid, everyone could benefit from a little bit of therapy. I should go myself."

He was right.

The therapist came to me, in my studio space in Nashville. I opened the door to greet her with my signature, platinum smile to keep things light. I wouldn't easily shatter my concrete facade… not for someone I didn't know.

I was surprised to find that therapy was more about questions than it was about answers. My therapist, Dr. Karen, began our first session by telling me a story of Socrates. Luckily, she loves history and philosophy as much as I do.

Dr. Karen taught me that, in his early career, Socrates fought as a combat soldier during the Peloponnesus War, against the Spartans. War was traumatic; the time changed him. After the war, Socrates devoted his life to the pursuit of knowledge... to the pursuit of truth.

He developed a reputation that spread throughout Greece. The name Socrates became synonymous with the idea of philosopher, or 'lover of wisdom.' He was widely considered to be the wisest man in all of the land.

Dr. Karen told me this story about Socrates:

"In ancient times, there was a city named Delphi, near Athens, that was thought to be the very center of the world. It was a sacred place... one where someone could communicate directly with the gods.

"Once the Oracle of Delphi was asked, *who is the wisest person in Greece?* The oracle declared, *Socrates!*" My therapist continued, "But Socrates refuted this. *It is impossible!* Socrates cried, *there is so much I don't know!*"

So, Socrates set about questioning everyone he could find— searching for someone who knew what was truly worthwhile in life. He searched high and low.

But, no one could give him a satisfactory answer. Each pretended to know something they did not.

"Finally," Dr. Karen continued, "Socrates realized that the Oracle might be right about him after all. *I guess I am the wisest man in Athens,* he concluded. See, Socrates alone, was prepared to admit his own ignorance... rather than pretend to know something he did not."

She continued, "*And all I know,* said Socrates, *is that I know nothing.*"

Socrates was notorious for using questions to help his students find answers. Dr. Karen related it to this parable: "Give a man a fish," she said, "and he will eat for a day; teach a man to fish, and he will eat for a lifetime."

Dr. Karen went on. "I like to think about my job like physical therapy. The therapist will give you the exercises and tell your muscles what to do... but she won't move your muscles for you."

"I could give you the answer, but you are not going to get stronger watching me lift your weights. You have got to work through this yourself. I'm here to help you— rationally and syllogistically— work through your problems so that you can arrive at a solution."

I could get behind that.

What I couldn't do, despite my most genuine efforts to do so, was define my problems for her. I couldn't even define them for myself.

Not quite sure what to say, I thought quietly for a moment. Finally, "I guess, generally, what advice would you give to your 21-year-old self?"

Hmmm, the psychiatrist hummed, then paused. "I'd tell her," Dr. Karen replied, "when you reach a fork in the road of life, stop and think... should I do what I think is expected of me, or what will most help me become the person I want to be?"

The person I *wanted* to be? She wasn't somebody I spent much time thinking about.

Sure, my diary entries from when I was a young girl told you that I wanted to be a singer: a Grammy award-winning singer who wrote her own songs.

I worked so damn hard at that dream. I tried to mold myself into what I thought everyone— my record label, my parents, my friends, my fans, my haters— wanted me to be. I think I subconsciously saw singing and songwriting as a... path to being loved by everybody.

But *being loved by everybody* isn't a type of person at all. It was a mirrorball. It was constructed. When the persona inevitably breaks, it shatters into a million tiny pieces... just fragments of a person, not a whole.

The spotlight had caused my persona to break. My soul— that never felt whole to begin with— lay in shattered pieces in a deep, dark corner of my gut.

People disappointed me, time after time. I disappointed others, despite my best attempts to do otherwise. I disappointed myself.

Oh yeah... and millions of people hated me so much that they felt the need to constantly berate me.

I still think about it, unable to fathom what all of that hate really looks like. I mean, of course, I saw the tweets…

Dr. Karen told me, "Imagine all of the mean Tweeters as little data points on a scatter plot. What color should we make them?"

"Black," I replied, "because they make me feel angry and dark." "Okay," she humored me. "All of those black dots are on the negative side of your equilibrium. They have a negative effect on your overall well-being."

"Sure," I said, humoring her.

My psychologist continued, "But, Rae… how many data points do you have on the other side of that equilibrium? Think about the little girls who listen to your music on the bus to school every day. Think of the people you inspire when you stand up for what you believe in. Just your album sales for *13*, alone, exceed the amount of mean tweets... three times over."

I thought about Newton and his damn law of equal and opposite forces. He has an uncanny way of popping up when I least expect it, swooping in to change my perspective.

"What if someone was taking data on your life right now?" Dr. Karen asked, "What would that look like? What would be the most important measurement to take?"

I thought about it. "I guess the most important measurement would be happiness, right?" She pressed further, "But, what is happiness? When have you felt genuinely happy?"

Happiness.

When have I felt true happiness?

Memories come flooding in:

Golden leaves, from trees rooted far beneath the Soho sidewalk, fall to the ground as I look out the windows towards the busy NYC streets. I'm sitting at a booth at Cafe Altro, sharing Prosciutto di Parma and a bottle of Malbec with Abbe. She's in town visiting me from college.

We haven't seen each other in a few months. Nothing has changed in that time.

I'm happy.

Above the rooftops, in a magical garden, I sit next to a cute boy, drinking cocktails out of red solo cups. It's dark, but his hand finds mine, for the first time. His fingers skim my fingers: mine curl around his in an interlace. I feel the electricity pulsing back and forth between us.

I'm happy.

My body trembles involuntarily. My nails dig into the plush velvet arm rests in anticipation as a faceless presenter finally announces, "And the Grammy for Album of the Year goes to..."

I hear my name blare out from the loudspeaker.

Mom is next to me, holding my hand. She squeezes it, hard. It hurts.

As I walk up to the stage to accept my award, I look out at the crowd. They're all standing.

They think I deserve this!

I'm happy.

But I realize that those are just moments. That happiness is fleeting. Those moments are the peak of the mountain, but life? Life is all about the hike.

Awards shows come and go. No number of gilded gramophones, diamond pyramids, golden microphones, or middle fingers statues can fill an empty void. Success is just a construct... not a true measure of your worth.

Dr. Karen reminded me, "I'm just here to guide you. It is important for you to find the answers for yourself."

We scheduled an appointment for the next week.

When I got home from the studio that night, I took out my pen and started writing. For the first time, a narrative— not a poem or a song— came out.

Imagine that someone has found a way, at every moment,
to rate your current overall well-being against your optimal well-being...
and data collection started the moment you were born.

Your current well-being, and thus, your reality is reduced to just a data
point. Those data points, which overtime would represent the trend of
your well-being, would tell a story. We could analyze your story by
plotting it on a linear graph and observing its patterns over time.
Hopefully, you'd see a steady trend upwards across your lifespan.
Small luck draws can spark a more positive upwards trend,
where bad luck may cause a downwards spiral.

But Isaac Newton taught me that when there are two opposing forces— and almost anything in life has opposing forces— energy will flow back to the state where they are balanced.

That state is called equilibrium, or most probable state. Overtime, you would expect, and probably want, your little data points to trend right around their equilibrium... because volatility is risky.

Maybe that is how the mystical idea of balance came to be.

I thought of something my mom used to say: *you are who you spend time with.*

I pictured my scatterplot. I visualized the ebb and flow of my own plotted points. I imagined how the data points of others (things, places, and people) could impact my own average. I thought about the bigger story of my life and continued to write:

I don't live in a vacuum.

There are an infinite amount of other data points in my story too, belonging to the people and ideas around me. Each of these little data points have a direct effect on my overall trend.

Can you visualize how a good relationship might have a positive impact on your overall well-being...

on your overall trend? Can you imagine how a
bad relationship might cause your average to trend down?

My mom used to say, "You are who you spend time with."
Later she added "... and you are who you think about."
I never understood what she meant by that.

I did now.

Friends. Lovers. Enemies.
Their stories all have an impact on yours. Their data points
average into your equilibrium. Sometimes it's difficult to objectively
assess the effect a person has on you at any given time.

Same is true with the bigger stories in your life, though,
like a promotion, inheritance, or retirement.

Something good happens, and your well-being starts to trend up:
something bad happens and you begin to trend down.
Life is chaotic, though... sometimes, the opposite of both rings true.

One thing is certain, however: time brings change.
Each moment brings a different environment,
cast of characters, or internal thoughts and feelings.

I thought that the happiest stories would gradually
and steadily trend upwards throughout the lifespan;
then, when you die, your story would end.

But, my life was like a rollercoaster.

As the coaster car crept up the tracks, I felt my stomach twisting in anticipation, flushed with hope of the excitement to come. Once I made it to the top, the ride paused, for just a moment, and I savored the view. Then, without warning, it plummeted. My stomach was left up in the sky... seven miles above.

My life consists of ebbs and flows,
of mercurial highs and devastating lows.

Positive things— like releasing my albums, winning a Grammy, moving
to New York City— likely led to a sharp ascent in my equilibrium.

Negative things— like getting humiliated on live television,
losing control of my story, and millions of people hating me— likely
caused my trend line to fall.

I've experienced downward spirals... as many of us have.
But, maybe that is just what happens when you get pulled
too far below your equilibrium... when you lose your balance.

The universe whispered in my ear, *Newton's law.*

For every action, there's an equal and opposite one.
If you are a big force, you should expect a like and opposing one.

Could Newton help explain some of my life's volatility? Does tragedy inevitably follow greatness? Is happiness a paradox?

Life might need to have its high and low points:
that's the law of nature. There is dissonance,
the area where our world is gardened;
then there are highs, where we reap the rewards.

Things tend to settle around equilibrium... if you're lucky.
But, I guess you have to ask yourself,
"Which is more important? Harmony or growth?"

Sure, people warned me:

"It's important to find a way to maintain balance with the craziness inevitably coming your way," Lizzie Starr told me, before my first tour. I never fully understood the implications of her sentiment, however.

Equilibrium. Balance. Symmetry.
Of course, we know those things are important,
but how can one apply that to life?

The next weekend, I traveled northeast to spend some quality time alone at Holiday House. I needed time to think.

On the drive to Rhode Island, my mind wandered to Rebekah Harkness... someone who, despite all the money, never seemed to be able to find balance.

Look where all of that money got her, I thought.

As I walked into the front doors of Holiday House, a man wearing a tool belt was walking out. "I left something for you on the table in the front entrance," he mentioned as he passed. "I was fixing the squeaky floorboard in the East wing today, and found some things hidden under it: letters and such. I thought you may be interested in them."

Was I ever!

I flipped through the pile of momentous: photos, letters, scrap bits of paper, and a rusted, big brass key. It was immediately clear that they were memorabilia of the home's previous owner. Rebekah. As I looked through the pile, I found letters from old lovers: Potsy, John.

For a moment, I paused. *Am I invading her privacy?* My conscious was always whispering in my ear.

But, I couldn't help myself. I was curious.

I continued my quest, only pausing to stare at a black and white photograph. Rebekah Harkness gazed back at me; beautiful and smiling. I felt chills tickle my spine. Spooked, I put her photograph aside. My attention was quickly brought to a scrap piece of note paper. On it, the following was scribbled and highlighted in fading yellow:

ϕ = *key to understanding the universe*

A secret code? The key to understanding the universe? ϕ?

I was intrigued. Searching for the answers, I spent time that weekend re-reading *Blue Blood*, Rebekah's biography.

This time, I payed far more attention than I did when the girls and I giggled over her story in the hot tub. This time, as I revisited the tragedy, I tried to really soak it in. I also searched for the symbol she left behind, hidden under the floorboards: ϕ.

I didn't find any secrets to the universe... but, upon re-read, I did come to a humbling realization. Rebekah's story really was not all that different from mine.

Rebekah Harkness likely had many happy moments—just like me— yet, her story still ended in tragedy.

What a legacy, I thought to myself.

But how could I be so sure that my story would end differently?

CHAPTER 13

THE AMERICAN DREAM

"Every action of our lives touches on some chord that will vibrate in eternity."
Edwin Hubble Chapin

Miss Weeks continued, "Time tells the best stories, Angel. A favorite of mine is about a mythical fairy named Moirai: the incarnation of destiny, the enforcer of natural order. I've heard many stories about her. In each, Moirai takes different forms. Typically, she is the spinner of thread. Golden thread.

This thread is our lifeline: our heartbeat, our equilibrium, and the map of our fate. As the years pass, life's threads tangle and twist together. They may become knotted or stretched. Stray pieces of thread may get left hanging, but the weaving never stops as the beautiful, spiraling patterns travel across oceans and lifetimes.

Call it what you want: luck, karma, cause and effect, the law of change. The duty of Moirai is to ensure that every being, mortal and divine, lives out their destiny as it was assigned to them by the laws of the universe.

Like gravity, karma is so basic, we often don't notice it. It is only when one strays too far from the path of their destiny that Moirai's guidance becomes impossible to ignore. I've seen her add coarse threads to many looms: causing storms, droughts, sickness, and madness.

Moirai would do anything to steer a stray ship back on course. But it's only when you are mindful— when you are open to the new threads as they appear— that you may be able to weave them together into a beautiful, brilliant story. Only then, can you begin to learn from life.

Moirai's threads aren't always obvious. When you are lucky enough to grab onto one, in your story or another, hold on for dear life. Follow the thread and see where it goes.

Looking back, you may begin to find patterns. You may then use those patterns to make sense of the chaos. *Hindsight is 20/20,* they say.

You may even be tempted to use those patterns to make predictions, judgements, or decisions about the world around you.

Beware, Angel. Rational logic can only take you so far.

Shit happens. Life is full of surprises.

It only takes an instant for the entire construct of your world to be irreparably altered. It only takes a moment to lose sight of your golden thread in the chaos.

Chaos transforms you and the world around you. Sometimes this is for the better; other times, for the worse. If you flow with the chaos, voluntarily, the outcome may be in your control; otherwise it may appear to be fated by the gods.

The moment the wedding bells rang— and the 30-year-old divorcée, Betty West, married into the legendary

Harkness family— Moirai began adding new threads to her loom. Betty was left with a chaotic display of colors.

But, Betty didn't notice.

Some called her spoiled.

Was she? Hard to say.

She never had to think too hard about finances. She didn't understand the true value that money has and infers.

Plus, Betty wasn't in a mindful state; she wasn't thinking about fate. She was too busy admiring her five-karat Tiffany wedding band, which to her felt more like a championship ring. A trophy... of the likes Betty had never won before.

Marrying Bill was the first-place prize; like mating with the goose that lay golden eggs. It proved to the world, once and for all, that always-runner-up Betty West was finally good enough.

Betty knew Bill was wealthy... but the money wasn't what drew her in. It was the prestige of the Harkness family name. Betty, however, was blind to the deep implication their story and money would have on her destiny.

Plus, Bill hadn't told her the full story. He only really opened up about his family that first night they got together, when he was drunk on the Ardea.

Before we go any further with Betty's story, Angel, there is something you must understand.

The Harkness family's story makes up the bedrock of the *American Dream*. It's not just that the roots of their family tree are buried hundreds of feet below the sandy shores of the Atlantic seaboard... the family is foundational to our present-day democracy, culture, and way of thinking.

For Bill's great- great- grandfather, Jack— who traveled to America aboard the Mayflower, in 1620— the *American Dream* was about opportunity and freedom."

You see, my dear reader, before Miss Weeks had ever heard the Harkness story, she knew of Jack. Over the years, Jack and his pilgrim friends have become all of our *honorary ancestors*. In America, we celebrate them each year, like clockwork— on the fourth Thursday in November.

The nanny, Miss Weeks, continued, "Over the years, for a variety of reasons, the story of the Mayflower pilgrims has become shrouded by legend, folklore, and propaganda. Most forget that Jack and his fellow passengers aboard the Mayflower were real people... who dreamed and sinned.

Many also forget that the pilgrims weren't the first settlers in America. With that, I'm not referring to the Native Americans.

Jamestown, Virginia was founded in 1607.

The first enslaved Africans were shipped over in 1619.

Pocahontas— a Native woman who's legacy has been taken over by the *American Dream*— was kidnapped by European colonists in 1613, seven years before the Mayflower pilgrims arrived in America.

Of course, in the movie, *Pocahontas*, Mickey Mouse got the story all wrong. The real Pocahontas never sang about the colors of the wind nor married John Smith.

In fact, she was kidnapped.

Remember, Angel, each time a story is re-told, details are abstracted. Thus, it is diligent to beware... even when told stories by people you feel you can trust, like Walt Disney.

After she was abducted by European settlers, Pocahontas converted to Christianity and moved to England.

Was this by choice or force?

Free will or destiny?

Is there a difference?

Pocahontas was but one of the many Natives living in the undeveloped lands of America when the first settlers arrived. For generations, the Native Americans had free reign over America's seashores, grassy plains, scorching deserts, and every place in between. Thousands of tribes flourished together in harmony.

Life for the Natives was about balance... not growth. Quality not quantity. For them, stories had healing power. Time was thought of as circular— the past is a route to the future, and the future is a route to the past.

The Native way of thinking painted a stark contrast to the Enlightened, rational way of thought.

When the Europeans got their first glimpse of the Native Americans, they did not see people with a valuable understanding of universal laws of nature. They saw heathens, barbarians; *primitive* people who had not been 'smart enough' to use and commoditize more than they needed.

"God have mercy on these less evolved humans," the European colonists cried!

Ah... the classic, Eurocentric way of thinking: growth is human's ultimate destiny. That dogma gave the European settlers the perceived right to determine the law of the land.

Survival of the fittest, they defended themselves!

We all know how that story played out[13].

But, the Native Americans understood a secret fundamental to life itself: the complex, interconnected nature of human existence.

Life is not rational, thus, can't be linear. The Native Americans knew, 'grow or die' is not a dogma that leads to longevity and happiness.

In fact, it may be one that leads to collective tragedy.

The very first European colonists who settled in America did so in the South— in lush, farmable Virginia. There, they raided Native American homelands, hoarded acres of property, and used a growing workforce of enslaved people to produce a surplus of tobacco.

The original settlers set up a caste system just like the one they left in England— one where the rich minority ruled over the enslaved or under-resourced majority.

This is how it has to be! The European settlers cried, *we have to protect ourselves! This is our destiny!*

Jack and his fellow passengers on the Mayflower originally set out for Virginia. Had they made it, they would have likely conformed to the social order. Instead, the pilgrims landed north, in Plymouth, Massachusetts, only because the ship had been drawn off course by storms, rough seas, and other tragedies.

It makes me wonder... *Moirai, was that you?*

---

[13] 9/10 Native Americans would be wiped out by European settlers in the coming centuries: through forced relocation, kidnapping, torture, murder, slavery, and plague.

In our stories, imaginations, and history books, the Mayflower pilgrims are model immigrants, pacifists, and pioneers who participated in a daring democratic experiment. They are heroes who pulled themselves up by the bootstraps to create a great nation from humble beginnings.

Some of that may be true.

But the real story is far more complex than that, Angel, as true stories often are. Just like in any true story, there is a fine and sometimes blurry line between hero and villain.

Compared to the horrors inflicted by colonists down south, Jack and his fellow Mayflower pilgrims looked like angels. In retrospect, their's made for the perfect cover-story... the ultimate national morale booster.

Who knows, Angel? Maybe the Mayflower myth was spread so that the real, tragic foundations of the *American Dream* could be swept under the rug.

The real story, though— the good and the bad— has been passed on through the generations in the Harkness family, thanks to Bill's great- great- grandfather, Jack. To the Harkness family, stories— and the knowledge they passed on — were as valuable as the money in their bank accounts.

Here it goes: the years leading up to the Mayflower's expedition were a strange time in Europe. Jack and the other pilgrims were a plucky bunch of saints and strangers. Risky, but revolutionary.

Some aimed to escape religious tyranny, others desired freedom and entrepreneurial opportunity. Many had a reputation in their hometowns of being irrational or mad.

Maybe it was true.

Their journey across the Atlantic would be dangerous. The Mayflower would be on largely uncharted waters for more than 50 days. The pilgrims didn't exactly know what was waiting for them on the other side.

It was a leap of faith to even assume there was an 'other side' to make it to. In shocking new science, Galileo only recently proved to the world that the Earth is not flat.

On September 16, 1620, the Mayflower set sail from the United Kingdom after a few months of setbacks. 132 souls were on board.

No heavier cargo had ever sailed across the Atlantic. The life-line of an empire was flowing west.

Jack Harkness was a single man and by no means wealthy. He only was able to make the journey to America because he was under the apprenticeship of a wealthy English merchant.

Lucky, wasn't he?

During the treacherous 66 days it took to cross the Atlantic and the harsh winter that greeted the pilgrims in America, I'm not so sure Jack Harkness would agree.

The Mayflower's journey was rough: characterized by storms, sickness, and starvation. The corridors were cramped. A few men fell overboard. Blown off course, the captain only had a compass to use as a guide.

Jack worried. What if they never saw land again?

Halfway through the journey, perhaps the worst trial of the Mayflower's voyage occurred: the ship's main support beam cracked during a storm, which threatened the ship with foundering. A spare beam was dragged from the hold to support the broken beam, to no avail.

The pilgrims panicked. What could they do?!

One thing was certain... they couldn't turn back to Europe. Turning back would mark defeat. It would be the end of their experiment. Any hope for a better future would disappear, like smoke in the wind.

Jack thought fast on his feet and came up with a solution. He took apart a shovel, one of the few tools he brought on the journey, and used a long iron screw to fix the broken beam.

His plan worked. The Mayflower was safe to carry on.

Without Jack, the Mayflower may have been lost at sea... never to be heard from again. Who knows what our story would be like if that had happened, Angel?

The Mayflower's journey was long and desolate. Jack's master tried to inspire the pilgrims with ideas of earthly grandeur and divine purpose. He told them the story of Moses; except in his version, America was the Promised Land and his fellow pilgrims were the chosen ones.

Still, morale was low. Until, one day, a child was born on the ship. Oceananis.

Oceananis was a symbol of hope to the hopeless. The pilgrims rejoiced! *Why would a baby be born if we were destined to die on the sea?*

A few weeks later, serving as look-out on the Mayflower's upper deck, Jack was the first to see it.

"Land! I see LAND!"

He then bravely volunteered to make the initial journey off the ship... into the unknown. 15 other men joined him. They were scared; many heard horror stories of vicious barbarians waiting for them on the shore.

The men waded through waist-high, salty-sea water. When he finally felt his feet upon solid land, Jack kissed the sandy ground.

Then he threw up.

The Mayflower arrived in the wrong location, over a month behind schedule. They landed in Plymouth in November. A harsh New England winter quickly approached.

Life was hard.

The pilgrims, scared of the Natives, couldn't make fire. Malnourished from the long voyage, most of the settlers had no store of body fat to maintain warmth during the bitter winter nights.

Many died.

Not Jack, though. According to Harkness family legend, Jack stayed strong. He and some of the others on Plymouth Rock made friends with the Native Americans; they learned from each other. The Natives taught the Europeans about harmony with nature, balance in business, and unity among all things.

Those ideals— along with liberty and justice for all— influenced Jack and the pilgrims as they established our nation's first democracy.

Jack began to find ultimate meaning in the story of the collective, rather than just in himself, the individual. During that time, Jack learned valuable lessons which have been passed down through the Harkness family for generations.

During the tumultuous voyage and years that followed, the pilgrims also realized something fundamental about the universe. Life is chaotic. In America, it would be up to them to create order. They created a government for themselves and postulated:

1. Order is needed amongst chaos.
2. Equal rights must reign supreme.
3. Some governments may be better than others... but any form of government is better than anarchy.

Harkness influence is at the very core of the ideals of democracy— which may be the real *American Dream*, Angel.

Betty quickly learned: the Harkness family was no ordinary family. They, like the other old-money families and super rich, rule the world. Wealthy people create the matrix which becomes collective reality.

When she married Bill, Betty was launched from the rigid, small-town world of Midwest debutante balls to a universe of infinite possibility. But, exploding into the universe in such a fashion also comes with great expectations.

Thus, she learned to walk on a tightrope.

At times, Betty found it difficult to maintain her charade of perfect woman; Bill was not always easy to please. He was clinically depressed and stuffy. Most of the time, he was a total mood killer. Betty had her suspicions that he was bipolar.

Some days— on the bad days— Bill reminded Betty of her father.

Instead of turning into an eggplant like Allen, Bill's anger shone in his eyes. Those eyes turned the most incredible shade of black when he was mad… as black as the shadows on a starless night.

Betty never knew exactly what kind of personality Bill would bring to the table… sometimes he loved on her like she never experienced before, other times he bowed out of parties that he promised her he'd attend.

Still, as Betty looked at her handsome beau, in his ascot and sports jacket, as he stood on the deck of the Ardea, she thought he was the most elegant and charming man in the whole, wild world. Bill Harkness was her king.

For a wedding gift, Bill bought Betty a house of her own. They picked the single biggest, most imposing structure in town... their very own castle on the hill. Holiday House.

That was a good day.

Holiday House became Betty's crown jewel... the ultimate symbol of her luxurious transformation. Perched upon the rocky cliff after which Watch Hill was named, the massive home loomed over every single person who underestimated Betty on her way to the top.

Great wealth, like the wealth Betty married into, can be tremendously empowering, Angel. It can afford its owners the exceptional opportunity to live their life however they please.

It is easy to think, once you have something, that you deserve it… it is easy to forget that it was largely a stroke of luck that helped you get there in the first place.

Betty adored spending her newfound money: on tickets for the Sunday matinee at the ballet, designer clothes, painting supplies, and instruments. Her children had the best toys money could buy. They took the most expensive lessons.

For the first time, Terry and Allen had a clearly defined world. Both loved their new stepfather. 'Uncle Bill.'

Uncle Bill got down on the floor and played with them. He listened to them. It was a Harkness family tradition to understand and support their children.

But they weren't really *his* kids.

So, Terry and Allen spent most of their time with nannies. Bright and early, each Monday morning, Bill and Betty yachted from Watch Hill to New York City. They stayed in an apartment downtown, near Bill's office. The couple returned to Watch Hill every Thursday.

During the week, the nannies ruled the roost. Terry and Allen completed schooling, took lessons, and played on their private beach.

As soon as Betty and Uncle Bill got back, it was family time. Together, the family dined at the finest restaurants. Betty and Bill drank the most expensive spirits. They never skipped dessert.

Bill had long-used the full-house life dealt him to create. When he was younger, he wrote a few books. They weren't about anything special. As he got older, he dabbled in poetry and music composition.

To pass the time, Bill and Betty created together. They wrote songs about giggles and feet. They played sports. They could be frequently found at the tennis or squash court, going skating or sailing. They spent loads of time making love.

Soon, Betty became pregnant. She gave birth to a beautiful little girl, named Edith, after Bill's mother. Everyone, especially Bill, rejoiced.

Bill found value in fostering a loving, supportive family. In the Harkness family, parents spent time with their children. With Edith's birth, his depression symptoms ceased and his engine revved.

"Our children are our future... our legacy!" Bill coached Betty.

Bill set the example and before long, Betty saw herself transform into a better mother.

Still, Holiday House was enormous— with eight kitchens and 21 bathrooms. Betty almost never had to see her children. Sometimes, they went weeks without their mother telling them she loved them.

See, Angel, how history repeats?

Terry, with her dark hair and chestnut shaped eyes, looked like her mother at that age. Striking. I think Betty hated her for it.

Allen's dark features highlighted mischievous, icy blue eyes... an epic foreshadowing of the monster inside.

Edith— the only true Harkness— was a delicate thing. Even as a newborn, she had wispy blonde hair and big opal eyes that pierced your heart.

For seven magical years, Bill and Betty ruled their kingdom. Everyone wanted an invite to Holiday House: the parties were unbelievable and the luckiest guests got to stay in one of the 22 guest rooms.

Queen Betty was more than happy to summon the commoners to her castle.

Guests— like Jane and Jack Heminway, politicians, dignitaries, artists, and the like— would join the couple for weekends in Watch Hill. They swam in the ocean and laid out by the pool. They enjoyed lazy mornings with a cup of coffee and the most astounding view.

Betty's insecurities never truly went away, but King Bill helped his queen feel confident around powerful people. He taught her to always believe in herself.

That was the Harkness secret, passed down through the generations: our world is made up of perception. Believing in yourself is the most important thing.

But as the years went by, it seemed as if Bill forgot that secret. It didn't seem like he believed in himself anymore.

Maybe his depression symptoms came back. Maybe he lost a sense of meaning.

Suddenly, all Bill wanted to do was wear his silk robe and slippers, and lounge around like a house cat. In the nighttime, he came more alive... but he also smoked like a chimney and drank like a fish.

"Betty," Bill croaked one night, after dinner. He was posed on a stool in the middle of Betty's art studio. Betty was hard at work on a clay sculpture of his naked form. She looked up to see Bill clutch at his chest, then collapse on the floor.

Betty, panicked, called for an ambulance. Next, she called Bill's private doctor... who made it to Holiday House before Emergency Services.

"Heart attack," the doctor proclaimed!

Bill was rushed to the hospital.

At the hospital, Bill's doctor pulled Betty aside for a stern discussion. "Your husband must change his ways. His heart cannot take any more strain. Limit the physical activity. Cut out the smoking and the drinking."

But, Angel… Bill wouldn't.

It almost seemed as if he wanted to die. Bill still played tennis and squash. He refused to take the elevator that Betty had installed for him, opting instead for the stairs. Each night, he still smoked a cigar and drank (at least) two glasses of scotch.

Deep down, I think Betty understood. That last summer in Watch Hill— the summer of 1954– she flew in dignitaries, heads of state, royalty, authors, philosophers, and priests. In June and July, they had dinner parties every night.

But, towards the end, it got harder and harder for Bill to breathe. By the beginning of August, no more guests were allowed in Holiday House. Doctor's orders.

Bill was banished to bed; chained to an oxygen tent. Betty read him stories and sang him songs. The children stayed away. Even little Edith, who was just six-years-old, could hardly bare to see her daddy in such a state.

Bill's story came to an end on cold, stormy Thursday.

The bedside monitor— which constantly beeped alongside Bill's heart— buzzed a steady, monotone pitch. Cardiac flatline. Bill's heart beat— the constant rhythm of his life— had ceased.

Other than that, the day was uneventful.

The funeral— hosted by Betty a few days later, in the backyard of Holiday House— was like a made-for-TV special. Family stayed in the mansion's guest suites. New York's trendiest traveled across the Hudson, dressed in astute black designs from the hottest white designers.

Distraught, Betty was only able to get out one sentence during the service.

"If it didn't end, what could have been?"

When Bill died, a part of Betty died too. She was devastated, but didn't have anyone to turn to. Bill was her best friend, confidant, and lover.

She spent most of her time sleeping at first. Betty dreamt of twisting sheets in the summer breeze, of ascots and sports coats, of giggles and feet.

Bill sailed into Betty's life and massively changed the course of her own ship. His influence steered her own, as the threads of their fate got woven together. Then, just like that, he was gone.

A week later, her father was gone, too. Massive stroke. Allen went to bed one night, then never woke up.

First Allen, then Bill, had suppressed a wild child deep within Betty; they created the order necessary to reign in a devil of chaos.

Now, both were gone. Dead, without warning.

With their deaths, Betty inherited both of their fortunes. Without their influence, she had no one standing in her way. Betty West could become the woman she had always wanted to be.

Bill Harkness changed Betty, inside and out; but, he was flawed, just like anyone. Betty never showed him her true self; she was too busy pretending and suppressing in order to appease him. Bill never saw her for who she really was, so he didn't realize that there were lessons she needed to learn. Lessons that the Harkness family passed down through the generations.

Bill's family understood: money can help make your wildest dreams come true. But, it can also complicate relationships, foster resentment, and create dependency. When one is wealthy, they must handle themselves in a different way. Poorly managed wealth can have dire consequences— both on your life and the lives of those around you.

When Bill sailed into Betty's life, he transformed her world. In equal and opposite fashion, in the storm that followed his death, her world was likely to undergo an equally volatile transformation.

But, Betty was still walking on that tightrope. What made anyone think she'd be able to find balance?

As Betty's world changed, she tried to numb the pain. Increasingly mindless, she lost sight of her golden thread. Her equilibrium.

Maybe it's when you lose sight of balance that the story becomes a tragedy. Who knows, my dear— if an individual force is great enough, maybe the story of the collective becomes a tragedy, too. Like the story of your family's legacy."

Miss Weeks peered at the girl, crumpled on the floor. She had fallen asleep... probably some time ago. The nanny sighed. Little did Angel know (little could she understand)... the story was about her family all along.

CHAPTER 14

LOVER

"Legacy. What is a legacy? It's planting seeds in a garden you never get to see."
Lin-Manuel Miranda, Hamilton

Legacy. What is a legacy?

Sure, I could sit on my golden throne as I sipped Rebekah Harkness's dirty tea, horrified by the tragedy… but maybe I needed to reframe her story.

More importantly, maybe I needed think about my own story. My own legacy.

Upon re-read of Rebekah's biography, I came to a frightening realization: one's legacy is nothing but the story that is written about them. Problematically, the stories written about you by other people are largely outside of your control.

I knew from personal experience.

The *Inquiring* often took great creative liberties to re-write my story. Subsequently I was labeled a snake. Millions of people decided I was 'cancelled.' My music, the thing most important to me, was completely disregarded. My legacy became synonymous with slut... with liar.

But my story wasn't over; the articles hadn't killed me yet.

In the spring, I prepared for the release of my next album: *Karma*. Work distracted me. I continued to see Dr. Karen, but Torò's motivations for the *Inquiring* article lived rent free in my mind. Over the years, he had become like family. His betrayal hurt.

My publicity scandals were like hurricanes. As the eye of the storm hit, I watched, helpless, as the bad press washed away my fair-weathered friends. After the storm, my beach was desolate. I felt lonely and withdrawn.

As spring became summer, I was stressed. Maybe I was even depressed. I started drinking more, especially after I finished the album. When I didn't have work to distract me— an album to work towards or another structured creative outlet— I found extra time on my hands.

Too much time... to think.

There was a lot on my mind: the way I looked (specifically, how much I weighed— I gained 10 lbs due to stress and was feeling more insecure than usual), my reputation, the success of my new album, and the upcoming tour.

Don't get me wrong, I was excited for the *Karma* tour. Live shows meant everything to me. International stadium tours had become my bread and butter. We had a sensational spectacle planned for the summer's tour.

I knew the fans would love it.

On my first international stadium tour, for *13*, each fan got a bracelet when they walked in the door. A few minutes into my performance, hands in the air, the fans cheered when they saw their bracelets magically light up.

From the stage, I looked out into the darkness. All I could see were their illuminated, twinkling bracelets— like bright stars in the vast night sky.

Some things for the *Karma* tour would be familiar; for example, we were bringing back the bracelets. This time, though, I sent my fans the bracelets early. They would serve as tickets and would be programmed by section... color-coordinated to the songs I was playing. The light show alone would be epic.

When I left for the tour, at the end of May, I had a gnawing pit in my stomach. It was the first time I left my apartment for a couple of months; under direction from my management team and publicist, I worked on *Karma* in isolation, from the comfort of my home studio. To avoid 'overexposure'

Trapped in my penthouse apartment, I felt like a wounded animal in hiding. My hunters? The paparazzi.

When I needed to venture out of my apartment, into the woods, I buffed my platinum smile and tried my hardest to appear cheery. If I was being honest with myself, however, that facade was just a mask that covered deep hurt and extreme perfectionism.

I still had this deep nagging feeling rooted in my subconscious: I desperately needed to be *good* enough. To do the right thing. To be liked by others.

So I pretended to be bulletproof.

The *Karma* tour came and went. It was spectacular, just as we intended it to be. The fans loved it. I loved it.

To an outsider, it probably seemed like Rae Harmonía was on the top of the world. In public, I appeared confident, sparkly, and fearless. But I was also dealing with a lot of negativity, obsession, compulsion, stress, and insecurity.

Over the past year, I had taken a tumble down the rabbit hole. I understood life in a different way.

For much of my career, I focused my attention on keeping my nose clean and staying out of trouble. I never voiced my opinions. I kept out of politics.

My dad encouraged this behavior. "Think about it, Rae. Would you rather be right, or would you rather be loved? Would you rather talk about politics, or would you rather have fans?"

Something shifted in my brain during the *Karma* tour though, and by the time I came home in early August, I had a new mindset. For the first time, I began to realize life wasn't about being as good as possible. It wasn't about pleasing as many people as possible.

Maybe life is about finding balance in all things— the good and the bad, I thought.

There were things that made me feel balanced: music, my family, Abbe, creativity. I was grateful for them, don't get me wrong, but I still lay awake at night with a gnawing hole in my heart. Something was missing.

I thought it might be love. True love.

Ever since I was a little girl, I clung to this Romantic idea: of a dashing Romeo who would swing into my forbidden castle, ready to save the day. Handsome and charming, he'd sweep me off my feet. Our love would be burning red; our story would transcend time and space.

Songs will be written about us for eternity, I thought.

As the years passed though— as I got more famous and my life became more dark and volatile— I became less certain that type of love story was possible for me.

How could I possibly write an ending to my story that anyone else could fit into... one that doesn't end in tragedy?

When everyone knows your name— when you have the money and fame (but also the bad press and false assumptions)— the chaos can manifest inside of you and all of your relationships.

That chaos can change you at the very core.

People thought they knew me... but they only knew the version of me I chose to show them. As I became more self-aware of that, I found myself struggling to relate to the people I loved most... even the people who made me feel balanced.

With that, my life felt even more chaotic.

My imbalance was evident as I wrote *Karma*. Creating this album felt different than my previous ones... almost like a mania. I felt desperate to respond to my haters... I longed to prove myself.

I worked on the record day and night. I was obsessed; it had to be perfect. I wrote hundreds of songs. Only 21 made the album.

During this time, all I thought about was *Karma* and my reputation. Thus, I had nothing else to talk to anyone about. My relationships all became stale.

Dr. Karen diagnosed me with a 'creative illness.[14]'

My past album, *13*, could be characterized by hyper-exposure and extreme extroversion. In an equal and opposite manner, with *Karma*, I found myself alone on a private island. I once wished upon the stars for space to myself... but isolation no longer seemed like heaven.

I don't know... maybe I just wasn't where the universe wanted me to be.

Somewhere deep in my subconscious, though, I thought love might take to where I was supposed to go. True love— the type that the greatest poets wrote about.

If I'm lucky, anyways, I thought.

Every now and again, I'd get an email from my publicist, telling me how a young entrepreneur or hot new model wanted to meet me. Sometimes I'd give it a chance, but it seemed as if I was stuck in a never-ending cycle. With each, the same, familiar story repeated:

The young entrepreneur and I met for dinner, undercover. Then for coffee. We both felt sparks... but when the press found out, he broke it off.

---

[14] The phenomenon of the "creative illness," as described by psychologist Henri Ellenberger in his massive study of the history of unconscious: a period of time, succeeding a period of intense preoccupation with an idea and search for a certain truth. Throughout the illness, the subject never loses the thread of his dominating preoccupation. The subject typically emerges from the ordeal with a permanent transformation in his personality and the conviction that he has discovered a great truth.

A few weeks later, the hot new model and I met for dinner. Then for brunch. I thought he was funny, and the feeling seemed to be mutual... but after a few disparaging tabloid articles, he broke it off. Again.

Time after time, the story was the same.

If I told anyone about a budding romance, the magic seemed to be inevitably ruined. Somehow the press would get ahold of the details and twist the story to help sell more papers.

Lather, rinse, repeat.

"It's just business, Kid." Torò told me.

Other people's 'business' often destroyed my sense of who I was... my self-story. It also destructed the thing I wanted the most. A solid relationship. Someone to share all of *this* with.

But, it was at that very moment of tragic desperation, the moment I felt all hope was lost, that my own love story started. My love story began at the moment I least expected it — as the best things often do— at a party where all of your dreams are supposed to come true. The Met Gala.

By now, though, America's Most Promiscuous Pop-star was fed-up with fairy tales. For the ball, I ditched the golden carriage; I no longer would play Cinderella.

New York City sparkled even brighter on the night of the Met Gala: the most luxurious, blockbuster event of the year, the jewel in the city's social crown. The crème-de-le-crème of high society attended the ball: Hollywood stars, runway models, fashion designers, journalists, business sharks, stock market savants. Everyone who was anyone was there.

Each was dressed to the nines. All wore extravagant costumes inspired by the evening's theme, 'Yin and Yang,' chosen by the party's host— esteemed editor-in-chief of Vogue magazine, Anna Wintour.

As our limo pulled up to the Metropolitan Museum of Art, my mind lingered back to when I first moved to New York... back when the city was my oyster.

I was such a different person back then, I thought to myself.

That girl— naive, but beautiful— was gone. Time had changed her; made her harder, colder. Her reputation had been destroyed. For better and for worse, parts of her— the parts that had made up her sense of self— had died.

One day, I looked in the mirror and realized the girl looking back wasn't one I knew.

A few days before the party, I said goodbye to the old Rhea forever. I chopped my long, curly locks and bleached my bob. For the gala, I embraced my reputation and went with a scandalous, all-black mini dress. Instead of my pop-star-perfect, cherry red lips, I decided on deep crimson.

My limo dropped us off at the entrance for the red carpet. I posed, begrudgingly, for paparazzi on the Met steps. My date for the evening, my publicist, never strayed far from my side.

I was mildly insecure in my scanty get-up, but buzzed with a devilish, electric energy. After the paparazzi photos, Anna Wintour greeted me. She was dressed spectacularly, as always— in screaming color.

"There's that smile I love, Ms. Harmonía," she purred, as I flashed her my platinum smile, "but your hair, Darling..." she trailed off with a grimace.

"I just cut it," I replied, sheepishly.

Anna tisked, but complemented me on my latest album, in her delightful English accent. "*Karma* inspired the theme of our gala this year. It's my most creative idea yet!"

I thanked her and we made small talk, but I soon found myself distracted. My eyes were drawn to a man milling in the crowd, waiting to enter the museum. He was tall and symmetrical; dark-haired, but with skin that glowed. He had the aura of a real-life angel.

Anna noticed me staring and whipped her head around to investigate. The man stood out. She immediately knew who I was distracted by.

Anna chuckled wisely. "Z is a quite the looker, isn't he? Apparently that is his full name— Z. We just met. Charming young man. He starred in a film this year... ah, I can't quite remember the name of it."

I don't know if I believe in love at first sight... but there was definitely some mystical, gravitational attraction between Z and I. As I mingled and exchanged pleasantries with the throng of celebrities, I pretended to look at the museum's art. I was blinded, however, by an explosive release of neurochemicals and hormones in my brain. I felt internal chaos. To keep my head above water in this uncharted territory, all of my attention sensors were keeping close tabs on Z.

Finally, I was in close enough vicinity to make initial contact. “Hi!” I pursed my crimson lips into a tight, nervous smile. “What’s your name?”

Fuck, I thought. *Could I have picked a worse opening line? I already know his...*

“Z,” he said, his voice deep. “And before you ask, yes that is my full name. I changed it after I got cast in *Call of Duty* last summer. The minute I read the script, I knew it would be a smash hit. I wanted to protect my personal life.” He laughed, “Which you may be able to relate to.”

His voice was like silk.

Z continued, “And I know you, of course. The one, the only... America’s favorite pop-star, Rae Harmonía!”

“I prefer Rhea, actually,” I responded, sharply.

What was I doing?

Z’s voice interrupted my thoughts: “Alright then, Rhea.” He emphasized my name. “It’s a pleasure to make your acquaintance.”

In front of the neoclassical painting, *The Death of Socrates,* Z took my hand daintily and bowed dramatically. The glass of wine I gulped down just before making contact hit me all at once. I laughed and laughed.

Our entire exchange lasted less than 3 minutes and I couldn’t tell you what else we talked about. Afterwards, I felt high. Euphoria coursed through my veins. Like Cupid stabbed me with an arrow, I was intrigued in a way I hadn’t felt since high school.

My publicist pulled me aside. She pulled out her iPhone and showed me an article. Z’s face smiled at me. The headline said:

Z: Hollywood's New Golden Boy?

She cautioned me, "Another actor, Rhea… easy, tiger."

Z's movie was one I hadn't seen, though. Looking back, maybe that's the explanation: mystery adds to intrigue. Or maybe it can be explained by science... all of those damned neurochemicals.

Or maybe it's as simple as fate: as if everything that happened in both of our lives was just leading us up to that very moment.

It's pretty to think about life like it's destined, isn't it?

Before the night ended, Z made his way back to me. "Rhea," he boomed, in his silky European accent. "I was hoping to get your number."

My phone lit up a few minutes after I got home.

Z: hey, what's up?

Me: Thinking about tonight. It was really great to meet you.

Z: same, Rhea.

I waited, as the three dots cycled on the bottom of my iPhone's screen. Z was typing. I closed my eyes.

Before he responded, I fell asleep. I woke up the next morning to these texts:

Z: i'm in NYC until the end of August. then I'm going home to Poland for the winter.

Z: let's see each other again, soon.

A few nights later, after I retired for the evening, a glow from my phone illuminated my entire bedroom once again. I jerked awake.

Z: hey, what are you up to tonight?

Under the covers and despite my horizontal status, my heart began to beat at an accelerated rate. Thoughts raced through my head, in an impressive speed, as I had an internal debate over how to respond.

Me: I'm just taking it easy. I made some cookies earlier.
Me: How about you?

Z: i'm at a bar with some friends. Lovers of Today.
Z: it's in East Village. that's not very far from you, is it?

Me: No— it's pretty close.
Me: I don't go to bars very often, though.
Me: Anytime I go anywhere, it turns into a circus.

Z: come meet us here.

Me: I want to, but I don't know if it's a good idea.

I waited.

I did really want to go. But it *really* wasn't a good idea.

First, I'd have to wake up my bodyguards. It was only 11pm. They may not yet be asleep, but they definitely thought they were done for the night.

Z didn't realize this about me yet, but Rae Harmonía couldn't just *do* something.

Any move I made outside of the house was an ordeal. I couldn't just go to the grocery store if I ran out of eggs to make some cookies; one of my bodyguards had to go for me. I couldn't just meet a friend for lunch, without a full-on security briefing beforehand.

After the slut scandals, my outings were limited and manufactured. I couldn't even go for a walk around Central Park unless it was okay'd by my publicist.

Meeting up with some guy (whom I didn't even know) at a dive bar, would not be a manufactured public outing that my publicist would approve of.

I knew there was only one way the story of tonight could end: in tragedy.

My mind was made up. I wasn't going to go.

Anyways, time was ticking. It had been ten minutes since Z had texted me last. An eternity.

My stomach sank as I concluded that Z had come to the same realization as me. I closed my eyes, and tried to calm my racing head and pounding heart. My room became illuminated, once again. I almost didn't look at the phone.

Go to sleep, I told myself.

You know how the story is going to play out.

Against my better judgement, I peaked at the screen.

Z triple-texted me.

Z: just talked to the bartender.

Z: he said you can come in through the back.

Z: my friends are cool. i promise, this won't be a circus.

I shut my eyes. Tight.

Okay... twist my arm, I thought.

I peeled back my comforter, and quickly changed out of my pajamas into all black jeans, a brown t-shirt, a beanie, and Doc Martens.

Incognito. Sort of.

I quietly made my way downstairs and noticed a dim glow coming from underneath my driver Mike's bedroom door. I tentatively knocked.

"Hey Mike! You still up?" I projected my whisper so that it could be heard behind the closed door. I heard some rustling, the scrape of Mike's chair, and finally his soft footsteps.

"Rae?" Mike asked in a raspy voice. It sounded like he had been smoking. "Why are you still awake?"

It was a valid question, typically I was in bed, asleep, by 10pm at the latest.

"I want to meet some friends at a bar," I told him.

Mike shot me an incredulous look. "At 11pm on a Thursday night?" he asked.

"Can you drive me there?"

"Did you wake up the rest of the guys?" Mike asked.

"No," I responded, impatiently. "I just need a ride."

Mike shot me another look. It said volumes.

"This is going to be fine, Mike. The bar knows I'm coming. We're going to keep it really low-key."

"Fine," he agreed, reluctantly.

The ride to East Village was mostly silent. I knew Mike thought I was being irresponsible, but I tried not to think about it. I got out my phone and scrolled through Instagram. I took deep breaths, to try and calm my shaking body.

As we drove down Avenue A, I remember feeling like I was hovering above my body... like an observer, just *watching* the events of the fateful evening unfold.

A massive neon heart— the sign for the bar— protruded from a discrete brick building and let Mike know that we had arrived. He pulled the car into an alley, right off of Seventh Street.

I immediately saw Z.

He was standing there, waiting for me. He was glowing, wearing dark jeans and Nikes. He looked like a Greek god.

Mike shot me another look— one of intrigue.

I ignored it, and quickly thanked him for the ride.

"I'll hang around the area. Just text me when you want me to pick you up," Mike called after me.

"Got it, Mike," I responded, as I hopped out of the car. "Thanks again."

Z led me into a small, dimly-lit speakeasy. As promised, the bar wasn't a circus. Only a few people were there. No one recognized me.

Z's friends were red-eyed in a corner booth. We chatted for a few minutes, but they were high and doing their own thing.

"Want a drink?" Z asked.

Behind the bar, the cocktail list was written on an old dressing room mirror. All of the cocktails were $13.00.

"This is my type of place," I giggled.

Z ordered for us. "*Handsome Devil* for me," he shot the bartender a million dollar grin, "and she'll have *Another Girl Another Planet*."

I laughed— *how fitting*— and pulled out my wallet.

"I've got you, Rhea," Z sang. "Put it on my tab."

After the colorful cocktails arrived, Z ushered me down a flight of stairs, and into a small brick hallway. It was glowing red, illuminated by old stop lights.

We sat on a small, wrought iron bench and sipped our cocktails. We talked about sports, Harry Potter, and the Beatles. Time passed quickly.

Soon, though, Z's friends found us... to tell us they were leaving.

"Sorry you came all the way to the East Village for my friends to bail," he glided, in his smooth European accent.

"It wasn't very far." I replied, "Plus, they were cool."

I liked his friends. They didn't gawk at me. They talked to me like I was a regular human... not Rae Harmonía, scandalous superstar.

I texted Mike to come pick me up.

Z cashed out at the bar, and we walked with his friends into the alley. An Uber was waiting to pick them up. Z lingered behind.

"They live near Madison Square Garden, but I've got a room at the Bowery" Z told me, "I could walk. It's not far from here… but, if you wouldn't mind driving me home, I would like to spend more time with you."

I quickly agreed, and couldn't help but smile.

Mike rolled back into the alley a few seconds later.

My driver rolled down the tinted window. "Where to?"

A jolt of adrenaline momentarily paralyzed me.

"Uh... I'm actually renting a place not too far from here," I stammered, "if you want to come check it out. There's a pretty sweet rooftop view. We can have another drink up there or even just some tea. I'm not tired yet."

"Sounds like a plan," Z replied. "Did you say earlier that you made cookies?"

"Chocolate chip."

"Do you have any left?"

"Sure do."

It was a dark and silent car ride back to the apartment. I felt Z's fingers graze my thigh. Then, his hand settled there. The hairs on my arms stood at attention, but I didn't move a muscle— I was afraid that he would pull his hand away.

Ten minutes later, Z was inside of the apartment, eating a chocolate chip cookie.

"This is legitimately the best cookie I have ever eaten," he told me.

Z was also impressed with my alcohol selection. It was quite the juxtaposition in comparison to my bare-boned rental. He volunteered to make us drinks.

"Anything but a lemon-drop," I replied, thinking back to Jimmy and the Palms.

"Do you like brandy?"

"I'm actually more of a whiskey gal."

Up on the roof, with the New York skyline as our view, we sipped on Z's hand-crafted whiskey-Sidecars... out of red solo cups (the only I could find in the rental). Z and I gazed at the twinkling lights of the city surrounding us.

"My mom used to tell me that the light inside of me shined brighter than all of the lights in New York," I confided. "When I was sad, I'd think about these lights. They gave me strength."

Z smiled. "That's a beautiful thing to tell a little girl."

That night, we shared stories. We talked about our hobbies and interests. I told him about my love of philosophy. Z told me that he loved math.

"Growing up, I never really understood math," I told him, "but my interest in it has grown lately. My tutor is convinced that math contains the rules that dictate truth in the universe," I told him, with a giggle.

I think I went downstairs first, to grab a thick blanket. It was chilly on the roof.

Z went down, next, to refill our drinks.

"Want to play 20 questions?" Z asked when he returned.

"Sure," I responded, but hesitantly.

I wasn't used to sharing so much with someone new. Any time a pop-star went too deep, the world always found out... and judged.

On his first question, Z dove right in. "What has been something you've been struggling with lately?"

I thought for a minute before replying. Shrugging my hesitations aside, I confessed, "I've been feeling stressed out lately... and a little empty, I guess? It's like I was the shiniest penny in a fountain full of shinny pennies, but I worry all the attention has caused me to rust."

I continued, "The spotlight changes your world in a way that you would never quite expect. It's overwhelming. It's hard to know what is real behind all of the noise."

"I've been struggling with that too," Z responded, "but, obviously on a different scale than you. Life can be crazy—like a rollercoaster. The highs feel so high, but the lows can feel like craters."

I knew the feeling.

We talked more. We shared secrets.

Time passed quickly.

Before the sun rose, under the cover of darkness, Z's hand found mine. We sat there in silence, fingers interlocked, and watched as the city became enlightened.

By the time the sun began to rise, we had fallen quiet. Z and I took in the views as the morning glow first cast light on the Statue of Liberty, then the bull statue on Wall Street.

The dark sky, once illuminated by the bright city lights, slowly brightened with the sun. Water-colored stripes of fiery orange and hazy pink were painted across the horizon.

My iPhone buzzed in my pocket, reminding me that reality was somewhere far away from this perfect moment on the roof. I checked the time: 6:10am.

"I'm glad we did this tonight. Thanks for coming over."

"This morning, you mean?" Z asked, with a tired laugh. He gathered his things and we left the rooftop.

Downstairs, Z made a hushed promise. "I'll text you later." Then, he quietly crept down the staircase and out the front door— careful not to alert Mike or the other live-in staff.

Hopefully no paparazzi see him, I thought.

Through the window, I watched him leave, then dove into my bed. Under the covers, I buzzed with a warm, golden energy. I knew Z was special. The night felt important. Still, I couldn't imagine the magnitude of change our love would bring to my life.

Love transforms everything around you— in a way you could never expect.

Our relationship wasn't easy at first. Z showed up when my reputation was at its worst... during a period of long, sleepless nights. My dreams became nightmares, with a highlight reel of embarrassing moments that played back in high-definition.

After Torò's betrayal, all of my relationships became rocky. I didn't know who I could trust.

That summer, satisfaction with my personal life was at an all time low. Despite that, Z and I found a way for our relationship to progress.

The key? It had to be kept secret.

I knew, once the press got ahold of it, everything would be ruined. Once the world started writing the story for us, our relationship would be divided... just like the noise of the world had divided me.

For the rest of August, Z and I met under the cover of nightfall, in secret, at my friend Keke's house in Kip's Bay. Keke was staying with her family in Calabasas for the month, so her secluded home by the water was the perfect lovers' hideaway. By the end of August, I snuck in through Keke's garden gate each night to meet up with Z.

As soon as our illicit affair began, though, it became clear— our story, too, was doomed to end. At the end of

August, Z returned home to Europe. For the first time in a relationship for me, a large ocean was doing the dividing... not the tabloids.

I was skeptical when he left.

You're crazy to think this will work, a voice in my head chided me.

But, Z and I still talked every day in September. September quickly became October. Z became a person I went to with problems. He was the first I told when *Karma* wasn't nominated for any Grammy's, to my utter despair and embarrassment. He was also the first person I told when the next tragedy struck.

My dear reader, that summer marked the start of something beautiful. In equal and opposite fashion, it marked the end of something that once was beautiful.

Toròʼs intentions for the slut scandals finally became clear. Early in October, Torò brought me into his office to warn me, "Gemini is merging with a SPAC[15]; we're going public, Kid!"

Torò communicated, in no uncertain terms, that my music was along for the ride; there was no way for the label to have the hype needed to trade on the stock exchange without it. "Gemini is more valuable as a whole with your master catalogue, Kid. You understand that right? It's just business." I began to protest, but Torò quickly shut me down.

---

15 A special purpose acquisition company (SPAC)— also known as a blank check company— is a company with no commercial operations that is formed strictly to raise capital through an initial public offering (IPO). They trade, at baseline, around $10/share.

"If you don't like it, you can buy some shares on the open market, get on the board, and have a say."

Sure, I thought. *But, how much will that cost me?!*

My heart felt like it was breaking. My mouth began to water with a thick, coppery saliva. *I might throw up.*

Once again, I had nothing to say. So I left Torò standing there, without even saying goodbye.

Once again, Torò betrayed me— someone he loved, someone he called family— in the name of the dollar. Anything goes, I guess, in the name of the *American Dream*.

Somehow, I didn't see it coming.

I spent so much time fuming. I hated Torò, I hated him! He was such a villain!

My mom's words came back to me, a whisper in my ear: *the classic drama of life, Baby! Who do you want to be? The tormentor, the rescuer, or the victim?*

Once more, I had been relegated to the role of victim. This time, it was in the story I anchored myself to: my music.

I almost let it pull me apart.

That fall, I spent a lot of time word-vomiting posion. Z listened carefully, but helped me reframe the story. He helped me realize the impact of sending someone hate. He reminded me of Newton's laws.

"What do you think the equal and opposite reaction of your hate might be, Rhea?" Z asked me.

He posited a good question.

It got me thinking: maybe the villain gets away with the persecuting *because* of all the hate being sent towards them. See, I've noticed this funny thing— almost every time I send hate towards someone, I find they end up getting love in return.

That summer was the apocalypse.

But, as life often goes, it was also the summer when things became clear. It was the summer I learned what love is; the summer I decided what I wanted my legacy to be; the summer that I learned what was important in life.

The most important thing is love.

I'm not sure I recognized the face of real love— transcendent love— until life stripped me of my shiny paint. Only when my mirrorball lay, shattered, on the floor and victory flag thrown, crumpled, in the garbage, could I see love for what it is.

Real love doesn't care how good you are. Real love doesn't care what the headlines say.

Real love is irrational.

Real love is about being the love you want to see in the world— both in its smaller and bigger stories. It is an authentic, divine appreciation for life in its many wonderful forms. It's a supreme attraction; the ultimate yin and yang.

Together, Z and I decided to write a real love story of our own... without outside influence or judgement. I had a feeling, deep in my bones, that our story would be an epic one. Transcendent, even.

Still, I didn't know if Z and my's relationship could handle what was coming next.

CHAPTER 15

SURREAL

"I think everybody should get rich and famous and do everything they've ever dreamed of... so they can see money is not the answer."
Jim Carrey

Angel slumbered while Miss Weeks continued to mutter her story, as if in a trance. "The summer of 1954 was a traumatic period in the life of Betty West Harkness. In what felt like an instant, the two most important men in her life were gone. Just as quickly, however, began the story of a new woman.

Betty's life was like a ladder tilted against the wall; each challenge she met with success led to a higher rung on the ladder. At the very top, the pinnacle of achievements: Betty married into one of the richest families on Earth.

Through the years, as she climbed the ladder and dodged life's obstacles, Betty found things to be easier when she employed this dogma: talk less and smile more. So, she often let the people around her— powerful men, like Bill and her father— do the thinking and decision-making for her.

But, as August slipped away, everything changed. Betty's reality blurred. The deaths of Bill and Allen meant a staggering loss of influence and massive gain of wealth... a potentially hazardous and volatile combination, especially for a girl like Betty West Harkness.

On August 12th, when Bill died, something died inside of Betty too. She lost her best friend, her confidante, and her lover. When her father died a week later, Betty wished upon a star... *please, God, take me too!*

On the last day of August, Betty almost got her wish when Hurricane Carol decimated Rhode Island. 125-mile-per-hour winds and 40-foot waves crashed into Watch Hill's sandy shores, tearing homes from their foundations and sweeping babies out to sea. The stores and businesses on Bay Street were destroyed. Atlantic Avenue was buried under eight-feet of sand.

New England declared a state of emergency.

By the time the hurricane ceased on September 1st, the destruction had been tallied: 49 died, 300 homes desecrated, and property damages were estimated at $500 million.

Betty, the nannies, and the children were able to hunker down in their New York City penthouse to escape the storm. Afterwards, when it was finally safe to return to Watch Hill, Betty assessed the damage. Holiday House made it through the hurricane. Unscathed.

Betty sat in a reading alcove and looked out a paned window to the sea. She saw a double rainbow on the horizon.

It's a sign from the universe, Betty thought. *Daylight comes again after every storm.*

With that, it was like Betty had been born anew. She stopped moping around, and decided to make something of the opportunity she had been given. To commemorate her metamorphosis, Betty dropped her maiden name entirely. She began going by her middle name, her late mother's name.

Rebekah.

On September 2nd, the day after the storm, the *Inquiring* ran this headline:

WORLD'S RICHEST WOMAN— newly widowed Rebekah Harkness— could sleep until noon or later each day and party all evening! Isn't she LUCKY?!

The world screams, *money doesn't buy happiness!* But, do our collective actions really line up with those words, Angel?

I see an invisible undercurrent that flows through American popular culture and our collective subconscious: money is what we need to reach our goals. Money is the key to help us find what we're all searching for: happiness, love, attention, power, security, or whatever it may be.

A common misperception? For people with money, life is easier.

Most don't understand the paradox of wealth: *having money* is typically associated with freedom, but too often those with *real money* find themselves prisoner to it. The dark side of wealth seems to be an inescapable cage, characterized by an ineffable desire for more, an inability to trust others, and sweeping social disconnect.

Of course, Rebekah felt a deep satisfaction when she first saw the astronomical, seven-figure number in her bank account. She quickly came to learn, however, that life was not made easier with her newly inherited fortunes.

In fact, Rebekah still found herself yearning for something just out of reach. She was driven, especially focused on music and the arts; but her drive seemed to be ignited by a desperate need to prove to the world that she deserved the cards life dealt.

I will use the opportunity life has given me to create, Rebekah thought, emulating her late husband, as she slaved away at the piano. She worked on music composition day and night. One afternoon, little Edith interrupted her mother's piano session. Rebekah had no time for her.

"What do you want?!" Rebekah snapped.

Rebekah's hard work culminated in a self-composed piece of music performed at Carnegie Hall— entitled *Safari*, and dedicated to Bill. Word got out afterwards, however, that Rebekah's teacher did most of the work... and that Rebekah just took the credit. A major social faux pas.

Rebekah produced a few catchy pop hits, which were relatively well-received. At first. Soon, the press became negative. Trying to forget, she traveled to France, Switzerland, and Haiti— always seeking out the most celebrated people and best teachers in each country.

The fall breeze became crisp as winter approached. In Watch Hill, Rebekah hibernated. De-motivated by the negative press, she retreated inwards. She soon found herself spiraling downwards.

To find a way out, she tried pills and alcohol. They numbed the pain, but also made the world foggy.

She bought herself shiny toys; she gave lavish gifts to others. "Expensive things make me feel expensive," Rebekah loved to say. That may have been true... but, the good vibes were fleeting. Something was missing.

Maybe it's someone that is missing, she thought, with a sigh. Trying to fill the void, Rebekah shifted her attention to interesting people. She flew in contemporary greats for the children's lessons: art from Dalí, music from McCartney, and theatre arts from Marilyn. Dalí, especially, often spent more time chatting with Rebekah than teaching Terry, Allen, or Edith— and Rebekah preferred it that way.

Rebekah took yoga from B.K.S. Iyengar twice a week. She discussed philosophy and theology over crepes and coffee with Simone de Beauvoir.

Judy Garland serenaded Rebekah and other famous guests with show tunes at Holiday House. Rebekah partied with Elizabeth Taylor and Richard Burton at Le Pavillon in New York. Grace Kelly and Prince Rainier invited Rebekah to their wedding in Monaco; Aristotle Onassis, Jackie's future husband, flirted with Rebekah the entire time.

Oh, the stories I could tell, Angel.

Oh, the gossip that's been spread.

Upon recount, the life of Rebekah Harkness more closely resembles a daytime soap opera. A Shakespearean drama, highlighted in epic detail and bold newspaper print.

But, I knew your grandmother in a different way than most, Angel; I saw something in her that others did not. The devil is in the details; but often, stories don't get the details just right.

Years later— when I began to work for Rebekah— I grew to know a woman obsessed with her self, appearance, and legacy. A woman who felt a desperate need to prove herself, but who was woefully insecure in her own artistic judgement. Someone who was unable to distinguish between daring innovation and vulgar excess... betwixt the foxes and the wolves.

Rebekah Harkness had made all of Betty West's wildest dreams come true. Everyone wanted to be her friend; she was the center of attention in any room she was in.

Rebekah was also so wealthy, that she was capable of fulfilling the wildest dreams of anyone who she came in contact with.

That's a dangerous position to be in, Angel.

Rebekah was underprepared, impressionable. Her new environment (the world stage) and massive wealth were like the deep sea: thrilling, mysterious, and potentially dangerous. As sharks set their traps to lead her down even darker paths, Rebekah followed, unassuming, like a minnow in school.

The poor girl had no one around to protect her. She didn't know who she could trust. So, she confided in anyone who would listen; never mindful to the games most were playing.

"Because I'm loaded," Rebekah complained to the children's fantastical, famed art teacher, Salvador Dalí, after one of their weekly art lessons in Watch Hill,"they all look at me and say, *show me!*" She moaned, "It's a very hard thing to face that nearly all people wish you ill."

"Mae," Dalí called her; a nickname. "Life is a game of perception; to master it, you must systemize their confusion."

Salvador Dalí was a flamboyant, Spanish-born, surrealist[16] artist— renowned for his technical skill, striking and bizarre artwork, and stiff, upwards-turned, handlebar mustache. He was a born performer; a man who needed (and thrived off) an audience.

Dalí was captivating... just as talented at self-promotion and money-making as he was at painting. His southwest-European accent was thick, but he had a way with words that threw you off just from pure amazement of its exquisiteness. He spoke in a scrambled language, but it was the tongue of genius.

Rebekah first heard of Dalí at a philanthropy event at the New York Museum of Modern Art. She was transfixed by Dalí's painting, *The Persistence of Memory*; mesmerized by the melting clocks and how Dalí managed to blur the line between dream-state and reality.

---

[16] Surrealism is an art movement— with undertones lying in geometry and modern physics— that began in France in the 1920s. It is characterized by dreamscapes and images that make the viewer question reality by delving into the depths of the subconscious. Surrealism, and Dalí himself, were extensively studied by Sigmund Freud. After meeting Dalí, Freud wrote, "For until now, I have been inclined to regard the surrealists, who apparently have adopted me as their patron saint, as complete fools. That young Spaniard, Dalí, with his candid fantastical eyes and undeniable technical mastery, has changed my estimate."

Rebekah peered at the shadow box frame containing Dalí's painting from afar. It felt like she was looking out at the sea from her reading alcove in Holiday House. Upon closer inspection, she realized that the view on the horizon was but a small piece of hyper-realistic artwork.

"Meticulous, isn't it?" The museum curator confided, "Dalí built the shadow box frame himself. I think he wanted you to feel as if you were *looking into the keyhole,* so to speak... this painting is a gateway into Dalí's bizarre reality."

When Rebekah gazed out at the Atlantic, she felt peace. But, when she looked into Dalí's window, she felt disturbed.

His scene was chaotic.

The drooping timepieces and swarming ants were jarring. Rebekah felt frightened, but fascinated, by the decay and entropy Dalí depicted.

Desperate to learn more, she invited him to Holiday House under the guise of overpriced art lessons for the children. When Dalí received the invitation, he saw opportunity with a glint in his eye.

Dalí was familiar with the well-off and fabulous. A master salesman, he knew the exact words necessary to charm any rich folk. Most were hypnotized by him; as they listened to his gibberish, their eyes filled with stars. He convinced many that Dalí (he always referred to himself in third-person) was an all-knowing, divine being.

When he came to Holiday House for the first time, the first things Rebekah noticed about Dalí were his ridiculously long eyelashes and tunnel-like, hazel eyes.

She complimented him. He returned the favor.

"Very beautiful, Dearie; extraordinarily good. Dalí doesn't like ugly people." The artist continued his aggressive rampage without pausing for a breath; "You spend too much time with ugly people, you become ugly yourself."

Rebekah swallowed, hard. She always was so insecure.

Dalí continued to ramble on, sharing with the heiress his obsessions: of psychoanalysis and Freud, atomic research and quantum mysticism, DNA and memory. An intelligent man, Dalí was on the quest to find Earthly perfection... back when he still believed in such a thing.

"Perfect beauty— transcendent glory— is attainable," Dalí proclaimed, with a deep, guttural trill.

"DaVinci taught us! Picasso taught us! Prince Matila Ghyka taught us!" Each sentence came out staccato; his voice got louder and louder.

Dalí was erratic; but, Rebekah vibrated at the same level. It was almost as if their imbalances balanced each other. Rebekah was the yin to Dalí's yang... and vice versa.

Each week, after the children's lesson, Dalí lingered longer and longer. After a few months of lessons, Dalí— and sometimes his wife, Gala— would stay in one of Holiday House's guest suites for days at a time.

Rebekah's private, cliffside beach reminded Dalí of his childhood on the coast of Spain, where he first fell in love with the ocean. Dalí was particularly fascinated by the rocks on the shore of his sacred childhood haven. The sun shone bright in the sky, casting shadows on them. Dalí noticed how life-like the rocks looked— almost like human faces. At just five or six-years old, Dalí sat on the beach for hours sketching the faces on the rocks.

As the shadows shifted with the passing of the sun, the faces on the rocks changed form. The tiny Dalí marveled at their metamorphosis. He recorded the changes he saw on his father's sketch pad, in striking detail.

Rebekah was fascinated by Dalí's stories and eclectic interests. Dalí was enchanted by Rebekah and her massive fortunes... so enthralled, in fact, he thought he might love her. Dalí told her so.

Rebekah ate it up, like his words were escargot.

It's a real shame, Angel. Rebekah couldn't have known any better... Gala certainly didn't warn her.

Dalí was notorious for destroying everything he loved.

Rebekah commissioned art from her friend: portraits of her and the children, custom jewelry, and the likes. She really padded his pockets; their relationship became increasingly symbiotic.

Rebekah told Dalí everything— her dreams and desires. Dalí told Rebekah exactly what she wanted to hear.

"Time will tell the world that Dalí was the greatest artist;" he preached, "and you, Mae, the most beautiful ballerina."

After Rebekah's failed music career, she had frequent nightmares. One night in Watch Hill, however, Rebekah had an incredible dream. In it, she found herself alone... a beautiful ballerina dancing on a large stage, in a massive, empty auditorium. A single spotlight shone on her.

As Rebekah twirled and leapt across the stage, her vision became blurry. She was crying; blinded by her tears. Something was wrong.

Suddenly, a second spotlight appeared on the stage. From the wings, came a dark figure. When he stepped into the light, Rebekah could see clearly. It was Rockefeller.

The man began to dance with her. After a few moments, their waltz caused the doors of the auditorium to blow open. The theatre glowed a hazy green, as a neon light shone from the lobby. Throngs of people began to mill in.

By the time their dance ended, the auditorium was packed. Rebekah and Rockefeller relished in the crowd's standing ovation. Rebekah was almost blown over by the roar of their applause.

They're all cheering for me, she thought! *They think I'm good enough!*

Rockefeller bowed, then stepped to the side. Rebekah curtsied, deeply. As she rose, she saw that the audience was throwing money at her.

$10 bills. $20 bills. $100!

Rebekah flashed a million dollar smile back at the crowd. She was over the moon. *They think I deserve this!*

When Rebekah woke the next morning, she declared, "I've had a revelation! I've figured out the perfect way to cement my legacy!"

Rebekah Harkness would become the most generous ballet patroness the dance world had ever seen.

Rebekah's people make some calls, and arranged her a meeting with Robert Joffrey, of the acclaimed Joffrey Ballet. Joffrey choreographed a show that Rebekah and Dalí attended that past June at Seattle's magnificent opera house.

Aida.

"I was a much better Aida," Rebekah boasted, a fib, during the performance's intermission.

Still, both Dalí and Rebekah were impressed by the show's spectacular choreography. After the show, the pair got a minute to speak with Joffrey himself. He shared stories from the tour that launched him to national fame; a tour cobbled together haphazardly, due to lack of funds. It consisted of six dancers and a borrowed station wagon.

Dalí was enthusiastic. "Extraordinary!"

Rebekah was also impressed.

Deep down, though, she felt guilty. Strange feelings always bubbled inside of the heiress whenever she heard of another's financial misfortune.

At the arranged meeting, Rebekah invited Joffrey and his dancers to Watch Hill for a paid summer workshop— a rare opportunity and welcome stress relief for the dancers. When Joffrey accepted, Rebekah was delighted. She prepared for their arrival as if she were hosting a summer camp.

As June's sun rose, Holiday House transformed into a multi-ring circus with dancers, visionaries, and other beautiful people flitting around. They impressed each other with fancy tricks; they compared scarlet letters.

Rebekah didn't have an impressive skill to show off. She did, however, have money to throw around.

Rebekah doted on the dancers like they were her children. Each had their own charge account. They traveled first-class to and from Watch Hill.

Rebekah took the dancers to Bergdorfs... she bought the men tuxedos and the women ball gowns. She catered almost every meal. On the weekends, she hosted frequent dinner parties. Dom Pérignon flowed freely. So freely, Rebekah even had the dancers clean her pool with it!

Even more dazzling than Rebekah's generosity (and garishness), was her remarkable ability to parade around sparkly people. Boy, were Joffrey and his dancers starstruck by some of her famous houseguests.

Dalí frequented Watch Hill that summer. He was transfixed by the dancers. *Gazelles*, he called them in admiration. Rebekah's son called the dancers *pixies,* in contempt. As the weather got warmer and Joffrey's dancers took over Watch Hill, the town's residents began to share in little Allen's frustrations.

The dancers could be seen from afar— pirouetting and leaping around on the lawn of Holiday House like marionettes. After a few weeks, Rebekah had the old Watch Hill firehouse turned into a studio. Then, to the horror of her neighbors, she had constructed on her lawn a gigantic blue Buckminster Fuller[17] geodesic dome... similar to the one Bucky would later construct at Epcot, in Walt Disney World.

Bucky, a good friend of Walt's, came to Watch Hill himself to install the practice dome. It was really a favor to

---

[17]R. Buckminster Fuller is hailed as "one of the greatest minds of our times." Bucky was renowned for his focus on fixing the problems of the collective. He developed innovative solutions that reflected the potential of geometry, patterns, and design to create technology that does "more with less". His ideas and work continue to influence new generations of designers, architects, scientists and artists working to create a sustainable planet.

Dalí... Walt Disney was indebted to Dalí following his work on *Fantasia,* many years prior.

When Rebekah inspected Bucky's finished product, she exclaimed, "Why, the dome is made out of nothing but triangles!" Bucky replied, "Everything in nature is made out of triangles, Rebekah... just like your practice dome. Triangles are nature's strongest shape."

Dalí nodded fervently as Bucky spoke.

"Our universe is full of math, of patterns. It's almost like our creator left puzzles for us to decode." Bucky laughed.

Dalí and Rebekah stared at him, starry-eyed.

"Geometry and math model entire systems... and how parts of those systems relate to the whole. How they work most efficiently! It's personal, for me. I'm reconstructing everything around me; I want my thoughts, plans, and the universe to work for me, not against me."

Dalí agreed. "Dalí has been talking about this for years, Bucky. Patterns! Geometry! DaVinci! Picasso!"

Bucky's words lingered in Rebekah's mind long after the innovator left Watch Hill... as summer drifted away, the practice dome was deconstructed, and the dancers migrated back to New York City.

Life is full of patterns to decode, Rebekah thought. *I need to make the things around me work for me, not against me.*

Much of the time Dalí spent in Watch Hill was under the guise of work. That summer, he began construction of a special, custom piece of art for Rebekah. The Chalice of Life: an 18-karat yellow gold urn, adorned with twisting tree roots, diamond branches, and sapphire butterflies. The urn twirled mechanically, like a tiny dancer in a music box. One day, the urn would hold Rebekah's ashes.

"Dalí's Chalice of Life is Mae West's *Holy Grail*[18]*:* it's how you live in beauty forever!"

Dalí had a strong belief in reincarnation: the transmigration of the soul after death. When he was young, his parents taught him that he was the incarnation of his older brother— a boy also named Salvador, who died nine months to the day before Dalí was born.

After Dalí told Rebekah the story of his family, he easily convinced her that she had been an Egyptian princess in a past life. "Cleopatra!" Dalí proclaimed. "In the Chalice of Life, Mae West will be a princess in her next life, too!"

That fall, Joffrey and the ballet headed east for an international tour on Rebekah's dime. They performed a ballet that Rebekah wrote herself— an extravagant performance(and thinly-veiled autobiography) entitled *Cindy*. It cost Rebekah over $500,000. She received an abysmal return on investment. Her financial advisors were furious.

Cindy opened in Dubai. Rebekah attended the opening night performance, but returned to New York early the next morning. The patroness planned to join Joffrey and his dancers for the last leg of their tour; she'd catch the finale in Cairo.

---

18 The *Holy Grail* is a folklore favorite; the quest of knights and Kings; the star of best-selling books and Hollywood movies. Different traditions, myths, stories, and religions say the *Holy Grail* is a cup, dish, or stone with miraculous powers that provide happiness, eternal youth, or infinite life.

"The gazelles are going to Egypt?" Dalí asked. "Oh! Dalí has always wanted to see the pyramids, Mae." He spoke rapidly, "Hollywood gets it wrong. DaVinci knew! Picasso knew! The Egyptians understood more about the universe than you could imagine."

"Could you teach me?" Rebekah asked her friend, full of hope. She was always on the lookout for an opportunity to become more interesting to others. When Dalí responded in the affirmative, she bought him a plane ticket, too.

In Egypt, Rebekah and her entourage of artists and gazelles explored history's greatest mysteries. The day after the tour's finale Rebekah rented a bus and drove the entire ballet through the Valley of the Kings. Then, they visited the Great Pyramids of Giza.

Rebekah, and especially Dalí, had a marvelous time.

Once the group returned from Egypt, though, Dalí began acting very strange indeed. It wasn't long before he stopped coming around... almost as quickly as he appeared.

Guess what his disappearance was over, Angel.

Escargot.

A month after they returned from Cairo, Rebekah hosted a dinner at Holiday House. It seemed normal enough, at first. Rebekah had been drinking, heavily... per usual. When the guests arrived, they enjoyed her open bar and hors d'oeuvres: escargot, water chestnuts, and broiled oysters.

As the 'dinner' went on, it soon became clear... no meal would be served. "Just the appetizers tonight, Darling," Rebekah told Dalí, dismissively, after he complained of being hungry.

Dalí was furious.

"Dalí is *sick* of eating slimy snails!" He stormed off.

Later that night, he bragged to a friend— "Dalí made something spectacular for the hag! The Chalice of Life! Dalí was going to give her a nice discount— only charge her $50,000." Dalí laughed maniacally. "Now? $250,000! The extra $200,000 will make up for tonight's piss-poor excuse for a dinner!"

His friend asked, "Won't Rebekah realize that you're swindling her?"

Dalí replied, "$250,000 to Mae West is similar to the spare change in your couch. She won't even notice."

Now, his sentiment wasn't exactly true— $250,000 is a sum that can contribute to the decline of any dwindling fortune. After Joffrey's tour, Rebekah's financial advisors had all but cut her off, due to her extravagant spending habits.

But, Rebekah couldn't help herself. Spending money was the thing she was best at, how she got the most attention. It seemed that her money was the only thing about her that others appreciated. Rebekah knew, in order for people to continue giving her attention, she had to continue spending.

Another paradox of wealth, Angel? More leads to more, in a vicious cycle. No amount is ever enough.

Many think that making money is addictive. Even more addicting? Spending money you haven't earned. The more of it you spend, the more you need to spend in order to get the same high.

In turn, family and friends start expecting more, but appreciating less. Standards become impossible to meet. Those with money lest be careful or they'll swiftly burn out.

The week after Dalí delivered Rebekah's *Holy Grail,* the quarter of a million dollar check she wrote him cleared. The next week, Dalí didn't show up for the children's art lessons; nor did he come the week after.

In fact, Dalí stopped visiting Watch Hill entirely. Rebekah called, but he always made an excuse. Before long, Dalí quit returning Rebekah's phone calls.

Rebekah was devastated. Dalí had become a deep part of her freshly constructed sense-of-self. One night, shortly after he stopped returning her calls, she couldn't sleep. She ran out onto the lawn, stood at the very edge of Watch Hill's rocky bluff, and screamed at the ocean. The inky water paid her no mind. It replied with a dull roar.

Rebekah didn't understand why her life was so painful. She thought, *I've always done what I'm supposed to do!*

To distract herself from the pain, Rebekah used drugs, booze, and the ballet. The more she distracted herself, the more erratic and volatile the story of her life became.

Rebekah married again, shortly after her and Dalí's friendship turned sour. This time it was to a doctor she met at a philanthropy event. A medical school professor.

Dr. Ben, the dancers called Rebekah's new beau.

Rebekah liked Ben. You know, she loved the attention he gave her. Still, before long, Rebekah began a sexual affair with a dancer; a homosexual dancer, nonetheless. It was inexplicable!

"Stress," was her excuse.

It wasn't long before things spiraled downwards with Joffrey's ballet, too. Increasingly insecure, Rebekah made a decision to change the name of the Joffrey Ballet to the Harkness Ballet. This culminated in a very public disagreement that caused irreparable damage to Rebekah's reputation in the dance world.

In an instant, Rebekah's dreams of a celebrated dance legacy were flushed down the toilet.

Within a few years, Rebekah and Dr. Ben were divorced. He heard about the insidious affair, of course, but Rebekah's increasingly excessive use of drugs and alcohol hammered the final nail in the coffin. Dr. Ben's lawyer served her the divorce papers.

As she got older, Rebekah found life to be lonely and depressing. She confided in a nanny, "It's just too hard to relate to anyone anymore!"

You see, Angel... large wealth gaps within societies lead to disassociation and conflict. It's inescapable.

Even on a small scale, vast wealth inequality— like Rebekah had with virtually anyone she came into contact with— creates a potentially tragic power dynamic. It makes it impossible to find harmony with others. It may make it impossible to find unity with one's self or the universe."

Miss Weeks sighed.

"Being the king is great fun 'til the tides inevitably turn, and the story ends in tragedy for everyone."

CHAPTER 16

IRRATIONAL

"A certain man put a pair of rabbits in a place surrounded on all sides by a wall. How many pairs of rabbits can be produced from that pair in a year if it is supposed that every month each pair begets a new pair which from the second month on becomes productive?"

Leonardo Pisano Bigollo (Fibonacci)

A tremendous storm brewed over the Atlantic. In Watch Hill, America's Most Promiscuous Pop-star slept fitfully. Her nightmarish slumber was interrupted by loud crashes and bright flashes, as if the gods in the cosmos were bowling. She woke with a start.

As if in a trance, I rose. The door of the master bedroom creaked slightly as I pushed it open. I crept down the stairs, as quiet as could be. When I got to the sliding door, it opened smoothly. I stepped out into the pouring rain.

I walked onto the terrace, then out to Holiday House's rolling lawn. I didn't stop until I reached the edge of the bluff; until I felt the wind beneath my toes.

My stomach dropped.

I stood at the same spot Rebekah Harkness stood crying fifty years before, and screamed out into the dark void. The ocean answered my cry with the roar of crashing waves.

I stood there sobbing. My nightgown was drenched; my scream was lost in the torrential downpour. I felt like a stranger to myself.

When had my dreams become a nightmare?

Lightening zapped, as if Zeus himself answered my cry. The god taunted me: *the nightmare began the day you signed on that dotted line. The day you became a commodity.*

Maybe it was true.

At the very least, my current existential crisis (and frequent nightmares) were courtesy of the main villain of that story. A saga that appeared on newsstands everywhere: *The Tragedy of America's Favorite Pop-star.*

I could imagine Torò chiding me, *don't be irrational, Kid.* But, I knew I wasn't being irrational.

Torò crossed the line.

This time, Torò's betrayal transcended that of him simply robbing me of control of my music and legacy. This time, his treachery was beyond slut scandals and public humiliation. This time, Torò compromised the thing most sacred to me: my first promising relationship.

When I woke up on the morning of the storm, my worst nightmares came true. I realized that Torò leaked to the *Inquiring* a story about me and Z, about the romance we decided to keep private. Torò exposed a relationship that I knew would be ruined once the world got a hold of it.

In typical Torò fashion, the article was equipped with scandalous photos: of me as I snuck in through Keke's garden gate, incognito; of Z and I cuddled close in her hot tub; and even of Z and I together— in bed, compromised— in one of Keke's guest suites.

Exposed like Aphrodite, I could imagine everyone (and their mothers) gawking at the pictures... laughing at me, embarrassed for me, disgusted by me.

I studied the photos. They were grainy; clearly from a security camera. *They must have come from Keke, herself.*

It wasn't until later that I learned the whole story: of Keke's disloyalty and Torò's final exploitative nail in the coffin before Gemini was listed on the New York Stock Exchange.

More on that later.

As I stood there hyperventilating, though, I didn't know anything. I just knew, deep in my bones, that Torò was behind the article.

How could Torò have gotten these pictures?

My mind started spinning. Out of control, I didn't know who I could trust. I couldn't muster the courage to call Z to tell him about the article. I felt sure that I knew what he would say: *our relationship never would have worked out anyways.* I couldn't have handled that rejection.

I couldn't even muster up the strength to call my mom, my brother, nor Abbe. In fact, I powered off my phone. As the screen went black, I decided that something in my life needed to change... or I would shut down, too.

The storm lasted three days, during which, there was no power in Watch Hill. I kept my phone powered off.

I had no contact with the outside world.

Instead, I turned inwards; to poetry, literature, and music. I looked far into the depths of the things I loved and was led down a rabbit hole that changed my life. It turns out that the key is like finding yarn in a wool ball... you just have to tug at the string and things become clear.

Without technology to distract me, I camped out in the old library of Holiday House. When she lived here, Rebekah filled the sky-high shelves with classics. I passed time pondering my life and reading books by candle-light.

I began with poetry. Specifically, that of William Butler Yeats, a genius and one of my favorite poets. In 1923, he won a Nobel prize for his *always inspired poetry, which in a highly artistic form gave expression to the spirit of a whole nation.*

Since discovering his work in high school, I've found myself emulating Yeats's spirit in my songwriting. He was one of the last great Romantic poets; he seemed to understand the transcendent and harmonious balance I sought in my own life.

Yeats was a genius. He made it clear through his poetry that he believed the very essence of intellect to be precision. I emulated that in my own life: through song-writing, planning my tours, and structuring my daily plans.

But, the life of a genius never is easy.

I found a Yeats biography tucked away and learned that much of the poet's inspiration came from Maud— his tall, blonde muse. She was equally as famous as he, known by her fervent fire for politics and glowing, natural beauty.

Their love affair was like a supernova. It lasted only five years, after which she quickly tied the knot with a different man. Yeats was heartbroken, but eventually married another woman. Still, Maud remained his muse throughout his career.

Life's funny like that.

To Yeats, poetry was a type of magic that allowed him to take off the physical and spiritual masks that caged him into the reality— or unreality— of his life's story. It allowed him to transcend, then construct his own story.

Poetry was the medium he used to work through and philosophize his complex thoughts— like a circular theory of life. I learned that Yeats also believed the universe could be understood by some secret code.

I turned the page, and saw it written in the margin... the same symbol found, by the maintenance man, under the floorboards: ϕ.

ϕ? Rebekah's secret code.

This was turning into a puzzle.

Searching for more answers, I dove into a book of Yeats's poetry. I found the same symbol, ϕ, written again in the margins of this poem:

Pythagoras planned it.
Why did the people stare?
His numbers, though they moved or seemed to move
In marble or in bronze, lacked character.
But boys and girls, pale from the imagined love
Of solitary beds, knew what they were,
That passion could bring character enough,
And pressed at midnight in some public place
Live lips upon a plummet-measured face
Empty eyeballs knew
That knowledge increases unreality, that
Mirror on mirror mirrored is all the show.

Jumping out at me, one word into *The Statues*, lay the key to unlocking the next part of my puzzle.

Pythagoras.

The name Pythagoras opened a door in my mind. I was transported back to Nashville... when I learned about the ancient philosopher from my tutor, Grace.

Grace taught me that Pythagoras has fascinated people throughout the ages... since before the time of Jesus Christ! Still, what is known about him is usually considered folklore vs. fact; myth vs. history.

Still, the Pythagorean theorem is probably the most famous equation in all of mathematics. The simple formula has fascinated some of history's greatest thinkers. Proofs for the theorem exist by Leonardo da Vinci, a 12-year-old Einstein, and U.S. President James Garfield.

Grace taught me about how Pythagoras used the knowledge gained from his travels to Egypt and Babylonia to establish a school in southern Italy, called the Semicircle of Pythagoras. It combined a focus on intellectual disciplines (like philosophy, mathematics, and astronomy) with religious studies and music.

Pythagoras wanted to live his best life; he wanted his students to live theirs. He taught them that the way to attain freedom in life is through rational behavior and philosophical living.

The scholars, above all else, strove to respect the harmonic, natural laws of our universe. To them, a failure to respect universal law was synonymous with sin, ugliness, and disorder. Respect for harmony opened their souls to intelligible beauty... and gave them access to the divine, beautiful order of the cosmos.

Universal laws, to the Pythagoreans, could only be understood using one thing: number. I heard Grace, just a whisper in my ear: *to Pythagoras, all was number.*

Grace taught me that not much is known— proven, anyways— about Pythagoras or his teachings. A fundamental pillar of the Pythagorean fraternity was secrecy. Pythagoras wrote almost nothing down. He believed that *abduction* was the only way to truly learn something.

"What is abduction?" I asked my tutor, unfamiliar.

She explained, "Abduction is a type of logic or reasoning. When you utilize deductive logic, you are led through the problem... you explore every detail. If the premise is true, the conclusion you come to is guaranteed true. An example:

Premise: all things with a heartbeat are mortal;
you have a heartbeat.
Conclusion: thus, you are mortal.

Grace continued, "When you utilize inductive logic, another type of reasoning, you are led into the problem. You go from the specific to the general. You piece together patterns, make a generalization, or infer a theory. The answer isn't certain, though, because you don't have an omnipresent view. Maybe the situation hasn't happened yet. An example:

Premise: all of the stories you have read are tragedies.
Conclusion: thus, all stories are tragedies.

Grace went on, “Is that premise true? Well, you can’t be sure... because no mortal has time to read all of life’s stories. Plus, all of life’s stories have yet to be written!

“Abductive logic, on the other hand, is when you are led away from reality— like through metaphor. One might use abductive logic in a situation where they will never know the true answer. Their abducted conclusion is the best, most-educated guess. An example:

Premise: all living things have a purpose.
Conclusion: thus, your life has purpose.

Trying to abduct meaning in my own life, I looked through Rebekah’s bookshelf until I found another book with tattered edges... this one, about Pythagoras. It was by a guy named Hubble.

I read:

After Pythagoras was exiled from Samos, he journeyed to Croton, where he found many young people yearning for inspiration. He gathered them together in a school— men and women alike. He told them stories and passed on his secrets.

At the school, there were secret practices, moral instruction, and a strict code of conduct. The Pythagoreans became like a cult: those who were ‘in the know’ were in the cult; those who didn’t know, were not.

The cult worshiped number.

Number, Pythagoras told his students, *is a language that whispers the secrets of the universe.*

Pythagoras found that numbers correspond with our natural principles and that their application to physical reality follows absolute and inescapable laws. It is through music that this connection between physical reality and metaphysical principles is evident.

Music is the proof: numbers can help us make sense of the blurry realm between subjectivity and objectivity.

Pythagoras thought about numbers in an unique way. For him, numbers represented qualities, not quantities. He predicted dehumanizing effects if the idea of number was ever reduced to quantity; he knew, in turn, quantity (not quality) would become the way to measure life's value.

Relatable, I thought.

As the years passed, I felt increasingly undervalued by my record label and society. It felt as if my worth had been reduced to how many record sales I managed or how much hype I could bring for the benefit of others.

But, I knew my life was worth so much more.

I continued reading about the Pythagorean secrets.

Pythagoras's knowledge was passed from one generation to the next by word of mouth. Pythagoras believed that it was only through oral teaching— the best medium for abduction— that he could help his students understand the meaning of their lives.

Pythagoras was particularly fascinated by the numbers: 1, 2, 3, and 4. Those were the numbers that appeared in the most harmonious musical ratios, of course. Music is unique because, unlike in math, the patterns embedded can bypass the brain and penetrate the soul directly. Music is the most natural path for learning.

For Pythagoras, The One is the underlying principle of number... the foundation of all things. The One is undifferentiated unity, the nature of ideas, the creator, the soul, the beautiful and the good, and justice and equality.

All things come from The One, yet The One emanates from nothing. The Pythagoreans postulated that everything in the universe, intelligible but not yet created, exists within The One.

From unity, though, comes two opposing powers.

I read how the number Two represents the dyad... duality, the tension of opposites.

I thought of Zeus; *a match made in heaven.*

Two is the beginning of multiplicity and strife; but it also brings for the first time the possibility of logos[19]. Duality begins when the knower (a human) is separated from the known (the universe).

The actuality of logos is achieved in the triad, or the number Three. Three joins together Two extremes, by bringing in a third term. In the process of binding Two together, the triad represents the nature of The One. Three is a microcosm of harmonious balance.

While Pythagoras primarily sought to increase the appreciation of the metaphysical and sacred aspects of number, he also laid the groundwork for modern technology and technical mastery of nature. He used number to understand how parts relate to the whole.

---

[19] Logos is an individual human's capacity for consciousness and communication. It comes from Ancient Greek, meaning "word," "reason," or "plan."

Nikola Tesla attributed much of his success to Pythagoras. As did Da Vinci, Einstein, Galileo, and Newton.

Pythagoras saw how music moved the world and compelled the spirit. He figured that numbers could be the key to knowledge that could raise one's soul to a higher level of immortality... the place where the soul re-becomes one with the divine.

The Pythagoreans believed that each of our souls were a 'torn off piece' of the universe or mere 'spark of cosmic fire,' held captive in dying bodies. They also believed in transmigration, or reincarnation; that the soul is immortal, but, unless released through a series of purifications and rights, it was doomed to a 'hard and deeply-grievous circle' of incarnations.

The purpose of life, to the Pythagoreans, was to break free of the bondage; to jump off the hamster wheel of earthly reincarnation, and join a cosmic, sublime level of harmony.

Pythagoras thought that in every being was the tetactrys— a combination of numbers 4, 3, 2, and 1. Human beings are like a mirrorball, each reflecting various fragments of the universe. In each, live all of the principles and divinity that constitute the greater cosmos.

I read: we each have the power of divinity within... but this doesn't set each human with the task of becoming divine. Rather, it is our job to become aware of the divine; to become aware of the universal principles that can be also found inside our souls.

Pythagoras believed you could achieve mindful divinity through philosophy of numbers. To him, philosophy was self-care for the soul. Philosophy was the soul's path towards immortality; the only way to re-join The One.

Some say that Pythagoras was the first to call himself a philosopher... he coined the word considering not a man who was simply wise (the greek word for 'wise,' was *sophos)* but, someone who loved wisdom.

Pythagoras's school in Croton was organized around the Muses— the goddesses of wisdom, learning, and culture. The students also worshipped the sun god, Apollo. Some historians have depicted Pythagoras as the son of Apollo, as evidenced by the shimmering, golden birthmark on his thigh.

Pythagoras wrote nothing, yet his influence was so great, the more attentive of his followers formed an elite, secretive cult: the Pythagoreans. Many others were envious.

The Pythagoreans were hunted down— their houses burned by mobs and their blood spilled into the streets. Everyone wanted to know their secrets. But, their lips were sealed for hundreds of years.

It is almost impossible to attribute, with certainty, any specific achievements to Pythagoras or to his followers. However, due to the overwhelming citations of Pythagoras as a source, there is no question that the Pythagoreans were responsible for a mingling of science, mathematics, philosophy of life, and religion that is unparalleled in history.

The Pythagoreans *were* the wonders of ancient Greece.

According to legend, the first Pythagorean to sell out was named Hubble. Hubble wrote what he knew in a book... that Plato bought for one hundred pounds of silver.

Plato— and many philosophers who followed, like Aristotle and Aurelius— turned Hubble's book and Pythagorean teachings into their life's work.

I turned the page of the Pythagoras book and noticed a faded, sepia photo wedged in the binding. The photo was of Rebekah... standing near the Great Pyramids of Giza? She stood next to a strange looking man with an upwards turned, handle-bar mustache.

On the back of the photo, was written the symbol: ϕ.

Another clue.

As if compelled by higher forces, I looked through Rebekah's collection until I found a book about the Great Pyramids. I read more:

The Great Pyramids of Giza, the last remaining wonder of the ancient world, were the tallest man-made structures for almost 4,000 years. The three pyramids are ginormous and were constructed with such remarkable mathematical precision that they would be a difficult feat by today's standards. But, the ancient Egyptians didn't have any of the conveniences of modern technology.

Over the years, conspiracy theories have emerged, trying to explain the mystery of the pyramids: of witchcraft, aliens, slave labor, advanced machines, and divinity.

Herodotus— the OG history book author— traveled to Egypt during his travels, and heard stories from the last great generation of Egyptian royalty: of ancient Egyptians chiseling stone from quarries and hauling the massive stones (as heavy as three semi-trucks) across hundreds of miles. Then, per Herodotus, the Egyptians constructed the pyramids with ramps and crane-like machines.

The only problem? Herodotus recorded these stories 2,000 years *after* the pyramids were built. He pieced together his account without our contemporary understanding of science. Plus, his account is logically impossible.

The father of lies, I thought with a laugh, as I recalled history class with Mr. Wade. *So, the story of mankind as written in history books is not the God-forsaken truth.*

I kept pulling at the string.

How could the ancient Egyptians— alive 2,000 years before even Pythagoras— have created something so massive without modern convenience? What kind of knowledge did they have that we don't?

I pulled out my laptop, quickly thanked the gods that I temporarily had power and that the WiFi worked, and went on YouTube. I found a documentary about the Mysteries of the Great Pyramids of Giza. It was more than three hours long, but had good reviews; so I settled on the couch with a blanket, notebook, and cup of tea.

It seems that most conspiracy theorists, and Egyptologists for that matter, use Herodotus's story as the foundation of theirs. I learned that there are large gaping holes in current Egyptology research; many of the conclusions drawn about the construction of the pyramids don't make sense.

For example, despite the precise measurements and smooth surfaces of the tunnels running through the interior of the Great Pyramids of Giza, Egyptologists believe the tunnels were constructed *after* the pyramids, via the digging and chiseling of stones. This hypothesis is illogical, due to on-site evidence.

Most also believe that the large granite stones that were 'used to construct the pyramids,' were each quarried from a distant location and transported to the perfect site near the Nile. Each block, however, weighed 360 tons.

According to legend, the Pyramids of Giza took 20,000 men 20 years to build. After finding a way to cut the granite, 1,200 men would be needed to transport each block from the quarry to the site of the pyramids. An impossible feat, given that 2,300,000 blocks were used to create the pyramids!

The most incredibly mystical thing about the pyramids, however, was the code inscribed within. It seems that the ancient Egyptians knew about (and encoded) specific modern mathematical measurements: the meter and other universal constants.

It's no wonder that many of the pyramid naysayers cry, *science fiction!* How could the pyramids be manmade, when all theories (and current understanding) lack a rational explanation?!

The documentary explained, and showed through digital animation, why the Egyptians must have had advanced knowledge of mathematics and measurement. They likely found a way to harness solar energy, then melted granite to produce a mixable concrete that they then poured into stone-like molds via assembly line. The pyramids were constructed using the secrets architects use today.

In fact— despite the disagreement of Egyptologists— *how* the pyramids were built might not be that mysterious at all... especially since we have the pyramids themselves as evidence. We just haven't been asking the right questions.

The *how* never was as important as the *why*.

Why pyramids? The Egyptians built the pyramids for a reason: because they knew how to build them. There's no other reason to construct such a thing... humans create what we know.

But, the burial practices in the Pharaonic tradition were undertaken not merely to provide a tomb for the physical body of the deceased, but also to construct a monument that retained the metaphysical knowledge which the person had mastered in his lifetime.

That knowledge was captured throughout the pyramid in precise mathematical ratios. The key was found through Pythagoras, I read, and through the number, phi[20]: Φ.

Rebekah's code... but, what's all the fuss about phi?

Phi is a number that gives logical proof of infinity. A mystical, irrational number— one that is impossible to write, because after the decimal place, the digits go on forever.

Over the centuries, a great deal of lore has built up around phi. Some has no basis in reality; others, might:

Phi is the equation for perfect beauty.
Phi is the philosopher's stone.
Phi is proof of God.

I know, I know. This all sounds crazy.

---

20 Phi, Φ, (~1.618) is an irrational number that has fascinated history's greatest thinkers. It has been called the "Divine Proportion," "Golden Section," "Golden Ratio," or "Golden Mean." Phi is closely associated with the Fibonacci sequence, numbers found in natural growth.

The first written record of phi came in the 17th century, when the Pythagorean theorem helped Johannes Kepler first discover many of the universe's secrets.

Johannes Kepler was a famous German mathematician and astronomer. His mentor was a philosophy professor and mathematician until the Comet of 1533 lit up Europe... and he then, like many others, shifted focus to astronomy. Kepler's mentor's guidance and meticulous observations were monumental in all of Johannes Kepler's discoveries.

When his mentor died, Kepler inherited a detailed portfolio of top-secret astronomical measurements. Then, he published quantitative evidence that disproved a popular notion at the time: the Earth is not the center of the universe. Everything does not revolve around the Earth... in fact, the Earth orbits the Sun.

At the time, Kepler's evidence was groundbreaking. He thought his findings would cement his claim to greatness; but he didn't realize that most stories end in tragedy.

Kepler churned out discovery after discovery.

People mocked him in the streets.

He uncovered that no two snowflakes were alike, understood gravity before Einstein, and developed the laws of planetary motion.

No respectable university would hire him.

To most in that age, God was mightier than the laws of nature and the Devil was more real and omnipresent than gravity. Most believed that the sun revolved around the Earth every twenty-four hours; that this perfect circular motion was set into being by an omnipotent creator pulling the strings of the universe.

Most of his peers were still trying to come to terms with the idea of a spherical Earth... all the while, Kepler continued to pursue greatness.

Kepler developed a new literary genre when he penned the first ever science fiction novela. Problem was, witch hunts were all the rage. Mysticism brought suspicion.

His mother, Katharina, was accused of witchcraft, sent to jail, and brought to trial. Kepler took over her defense. He approached the trial like he did his work.

It was one of the first of its kind: science vs. superstition. Facts, evidence, and rationality vs. cries of *Satan*, irrational claims of causing inhumane pain to children, and Katharina's own son-in-law accusing her of sorcery.

Kepler won.

He built his mother's case like he constructed his scientific theories... and deconstructed the prosecution's arguments one by one, with evidence. His position was indisputable.

Katharina was cleared of all charges, but was exiled from her village. The stigma that went along with witchcraft was too much to bear. She soon died of shame.

Kepler soon died, too. But, before he passed, he had another great discovery to unearth. He found a key to understanding the universe, by using the Pythagorean theorem to understand the relationships between celestial objects. Upon calculation, phi was the ratio found when measuring the distances between all planets.

Kepler theorized phi might be found at the beginning, center, and end of the universe. He actually gave it the name phi in honor of Phidias, who's use of the golden ratio is evident throughout the architecture of his famed Greek Parthenon... the same Parthenon of which there is a replica in Nashville's Centennial Park.

My favorite place, I thought. *What a coincidence.*

I read that Kepler also referred to phi as the 'Divine Proportion,' and wrote:

I've found a number so irrational and rare, it could never be written down in its entirety. Its terms go on forever after the decimal point without repeating. It can be proven with logic.

The realization that there exist irrational numbers and that they can be logically proven, caused a true philosophical crisis in the minds fresh into the Scientific Revolution. Irrationality, prior to this, was thought to be unnatural and illogical. The product of witchcraft, even!

Funny enough, before Kepler, phi was hidden in plain sight. In the 1200s, Fibonacci wrote a riddle (which is found at the beginning of this chapter), that can be used to find phi. The answer to the riddle is a sequence of numbers, now known as the Fibonacci sequence.

The Fibonacci sequence explains exponential growth in man-made and natural phenomena. It is mystical because, in the sequence, every subsequent number is found by adding together the two preceding numbers. When you divide a larger Fibonacci number by the one directly before it in the sequence, you get a number that gets closer and closer to phi as the Fibonacci sequence grows 'til infinity.

That's right. Just like the number phi, the Fibonacci sequence goes on for forever.

The Fibonacci sequence and phi have been long admired by thinkers and creatives. It is theorized to be the secret of the Pythagoreans.

Phi may be encrypted in the music of Bach, the art of DaVinci (and Dalí), the patents of Tesla, theories of chaos and probability, and some of the greatest American poetry and literature... but no one can explain *why* this number is echoed so clearly.

There's speculation of course: phi is a transcendent idea form; phi is the evergreen, harmonious balance that makes in the triad, the microcosm that mimic The One.

Either way, it's indisputable: Φ is found in proportions across the universe; it is found in the infinite.

Phi. The Golden Ratio. The first rationally-proved irrational number. Pythagorean's theorem was the key to unlocking one of the greatest mysteries of all time.

Causation or correlation, phi has the uncanniest way of popping up where it is least expected— throughout music theory, in spiral staircases, galaxies, butterflies, the most beautiful faces, the most famous art, heartbeats, DNA, ancient architecture, the rise and fall of the stock market... and it was an universal constant found throughout the Great Pyramids of Giza.

It was the secret the Egyptians were trying to pass on.

All of a sudden, a wave of exhaustion hit me.

I closed the book.

Later that night, I took a bath. I think I went to sleep early. Only upon second glance, does that day became important.

The day I learned about phi was the day I became a true poet: a philosopher.

It seems that philosophy is written in a grand book—the universe— which stands continually open to our gaze. It cannot be understood, however, if one does not first learn to see the symmetries, comprehend the language, and interpret the symbols in which it is written.

An understanding can be achieved through number; then, it can be depicted using triangles, circles, and other geometrical figures. It has been passed down through the generations in words, music, architecture, and art.

Without geometry, it would be impossible for humans to understand a single word of the universe. Without number, humankind is just wandering about in a dark labyrinth. Without math, there could be no order in our chaos.

Don't fear, though.

If you're curious enough, you can find the answers. I've come to learn, they're buried in the depths of any story you love.

CHAPTER 17

LEGACY

"Madame, all stories, if continued far enough, end in death, and he is no true-story teller who would keep that from you."
Ernest Hemingway

It was uterine cancer." Miss Weeks went on, "The doctor warned Rebekah, "The tumor is the size of a football."

Many years had passed since Dalí, Bucky, Joffrey, and Dr. Ben roamed the halls of Holiday House. During that time, Rebekah got lost deeper and deeper in life's labyrinth. She dulled her confusion and deep pain with illicit substances, lovers, and money.

The universe— *or was it Moriai?*— gave Rebekah many signs... so many opportunities to get herself out of the spiraling black hole she had trapped herself in.

I guess she didn't see them, Angel.

As her children grew up and left the nest, Rebekah passed her time popping pills, guzzling pink Bacardi, and pouring an extravagant amount of her dwindling fortune into the ballet. After she and Joffrey split, Rebekah spent millions trying to make something of the Harkness Ballet... with little success.

Sure, the dancers were always given wonderful reviews. But, reporters seemed far more intrigued by the drama happening behind the scenes: Rebekah's inability to hold her liquor, increasingly frequent falls, promiscuity... and, worst of all, her extravagant spending during a nation-wide economic downturn.

With the negative press directed towards her, once again, Rebekah spiraled downwards. She had no sense of purpose. She didn't know who she could trust.

She always was such a God-awful judge of character.

Rebekah spent most of her time (and millions of dollars) searching for purpose in others... in everyone and everything except her kids, of course. When the children— Allen, Terry Anne, and Edith— became adults, the family did not keep in close contact.

Like his mother, little Allen grew up splashed on the front page; his misdeeds were highlighted in the bold ink of newspaper headlines. A few years before Rebekah's diagnosis, Allen went to prison— for murder.

His mother wouldn't post his bail money.

After that, Rebekah never heard from Allen.

Rebekah married and divorced. Again.

This time, it was to another doctor: Dr. Love. He was a 30-year-old gynecologist, who was closer in age to her daughters than Rebekah. Terry and Edith found out about their mother's fourth marriage via *Time* magazine.

Dr. Love gave Rebekah the nickname *Karma*— which she was positively delighted by— and he frequently injected her with a 'Vitamin B' concoction that many suspected contained cocaine. Dr. Love didn't notice any cancer symptoms.

"Stage 4." A cancer doctor told her, a few months after Rebekah's final divorce. "It's terminal. I'd give it 10 months."

Rebekah cried on her butler's shoulder. He was the one she had chosen to accompany her to the appointment.

She got a second opinion. At that appointment a different doctor still told her that, with the way the tumor was blocking her intestine, she probably only had ten days to live.

"Ten days to live?!" Rebekah screeched to the housemaid who had accompanied her on this appointment. "I thought I had at least ten months!"

Frantic, Rebekah tried desperately to get ahold of her children. Before her death loomed, she couldn't have been bothered to think about them. Now, she was resentful; she despised that her children didn't rush to be by her side.

The ten days passed. Slowly.

Rebekah sat in the top alcove of Holiday House. She looked out at the sea and watched old movies (but, she almost never made it through one without dozing off). She reminisced with staff members. On the tenth day, when she hadn't yet perished, the house staff threw Rebekah a party. Edith nor Terry made it to Rhode Island in time.

"You're a survivor, Ma'am," the butler exclaimed!

Those last few months in Watch Hill were a madhouse: controversy over the will, cat-fights, manipulation, and a ton of pills and pink booze. *Oh, my!*

Edith and Terry finally made it to Holiday House... reluctantly. They watched in detached despair as, in the weeks leading to her death, their mother got weaker and weaker.

Rebekah went through the seven stages of grief. As she lay dying, she became calmer, softer. I think Rebekah almost reached a transcendent place of acceptance and hope... but she was still far too preoccupied by what other people thought of her.

She competed for attention 'til the very end.

Rebekah fretted over her looks, most of all. The doctors had her on all sorts of experimental treatments and Rebekah rapidly lost her hair. She had her lawyer bring over some wigs to cover up.

Edith couldn't help it... when she first saw her mother wearing a lopsided wig, Edith began to cry. Rebekah looked so unlike herself.

Rebekah patted Edith on the shoulder. She soothed, "Don't cry for me, baby bird. We've been here before and we'll be here again."

If the cancer didn't kill Rebekah, the stress over her will may have. There was such discontent over that damn will.

'Til her very last day, Rebekah wanted to please the people she thought mattered. She knew she was going to die, but she still tried to make everyone happy. Rebekah was happiest when she basked in the love from those around her... the people she thought were important.

But, any happy last moments were contrasted by a swift and brutal end for the heiress... who died far too young.

When she died, there was a hodgepodge of people at her side: Edith, Terry, the housekeepers and other staff, doctors, lawyers, her homosexual lover, hangers-on, and the like. Her death-bed was complete chaos. Everyone was running around, still signing wills, and trying on different wigs!

Despite all of the tragedies surrounding the life and death of Rebekah Betty West Harkness, the most tragic story was that of her journey in motherhood. Her children were the true victims of the story.

> Their lives, *calamitous*.
> Rebekah's legacy, *tarnished*.
> The Harkness dynasty, *destroyed*.
> Allen, *incarcerated*.
> Edith and Terry, *deceased*.
> Their stories, *disturbing*.

Let me tell you about it, Angel.

From the moment she was born, Edith was just a prized possession for Rebekah to show off; a perfect daughter from the perfect marriage. Edith resembled a China doll. She had soft, classic features and full head of blonde hair. To the delight of Rebekah, as Edith grew, she became even more beautiful.

But, little Edith always felt like just another *thing* her mother owned.

Edith's soul was wise beyond its years. She was empathetic and inquisitive. At a friend's birthday party, the other six-year-olds were off playing... but Rebekah found Edith in the corner, totally engrossed in a book. Rebekah told me, with an incredulous laugh, that the book was *A Tale of Two Cities*.

It was clear to anyone who knew them: Edith and her mother lived in two different realities. Edith was modest, unpretentious, and painfully embarrassed by her family's riches. Rebekah was garish, overbearing, and lived with her head in a bubble.

It was a top priority of Rebekah's that Edith looked perfect at all times. She also made sure Edith was always on her best behavior.

"Prim and proper, my little bird," Rebekah coached.

As a little girl, Edith often felt like she was caged into this life; bound with chains to other's expectations.

Edith was quite likable; still, she felt completely alone in the world. Most of Edith's time was spent by herself, in a little 'clubhouse' she called the Cockpit— a small room that jutted out from the third floor of Holiday House and boasted a dramatic 180-degree view of the Rhode Island coast.

She spent hours up in the Cockpit. She read *Peter Pan* (over and over), wrote in her journal, and wished she were really a bird.

Edith desired, more than anything, to fly far away.

Sometimes, under the cover of nightfall, Edith would sneak out of the house. She was seen on multiple occasions on the lawn after midnight, her dancing figure but a silhouette in the moonlight.

Little Edith was just seven years old when Bill died.

After her father's death, her mother was never the same. The children were homeschooled. Other than with her half-siblings, Edith had almost no contact with peers her own age. She was enrolled in the best lessons, she had the most fabulous teachers; but, the little heiress didn't have anyone to talk to.

When she was nine, Edith tried to commit suicide.

One day, the small girl gave her housekeeper a corked bottle. Inside was a note.

"Will you throw this in the ocean for me?" Edith asked the maid, as soft and innocent as could be.

Edith then turned around and slowly made the ascent to her private Jack and Jill bathroom... where 45 pills of aspirin waited for her.

The housekeeper stood by until the girl was gone; then, she opened the bottle. The note said:

When someone finds this bottle, I'll be dead.

Panicked, the housekeeper alerted the nannies. The nannies found Edith lying on the bathroom floor, her beautiful blonde hair splayed around her head like a halo.

An empty pill bottle lay next to her, with the cap off.

Edith was rushed to the hospital and her stomach was pumped. She woke up the next morning, groggy but alive.

"No harm, no foul," the nanny proclaimed!

The doctors called it an accident. "Nine-year-old girls don't try to kill themselves," the attending physician declared. When Edith got home from the hospital, the incident was never mentioned again.

At the age of 12, Edith, who was having a meltdown, threatened to jump out of the window. Her nanny, exasperated with the girl's behavior, egged her on.

"Go ahead; do it," the nanny taunted.

So, Edith did.

The fall would have been fatal... if it weren't for the massive snow storm that had hit the East coast a few days before. When Edith jumped, she fell into a soft snowbank.

"Lucky," the doctors called her. "This little girl should be dead."

Rebekah was infuriated with Edith's behavior! She discussed her child's issues with her book club. "The girl's plan will inevitably be successful someday." The heiress mused, "But, is there a chic way to go?"

When Rebekah commissioned Dalí to paint a picture of Edith, she didn't expect the final product to show her youngest daughter enclosed in a golden aviary. Nonetheless, Rebekah was delighted by the painting and showed it off to all her friends.

"Dalí made Edith look so angelic," the heiress bragged; "just like a little bird!"

Rebekah's friends whispered behind her back. "What a sad sight... a tortured girl trapped in a gilded birdcage."

You know, maybe we're all trapped, Angel.

Sometimes, life's cages can be invisible.

As Edith grew older, likely due to similar reasons, she fell into the same alcoholic tendencies as Rebekah. Edith gained weight. She went to rehab multiple times. She made bad decisions about men. She spent her lavish fortunes.

Edith barely made it to her mother's bedside before she died. She always felt so judged by her mother. Embarrassed largely due to her weight and appearance, Edith hadn't seen Rebekah in half a decade.

But, by the time of her mother's diagnosis, Edith's life had begun a transformation. She stopped the drinking. She lost the weight. When Rebekah finally saw her youngest daughter, she was delighted.

"My beautiful bird," the dying woman cooed.

It was only on Rebekah's deathbed that Edith finally achieved her mother's acceptance and attention. Edith had always wanted Rebekah's approval.

After her mother's death, Edith helped clean Rebekah's apartment. Precious art began disappearing from the walls a few minutes after Rebekah's heart stopped beating. I know, for a fact, that the homosexual lover stole away with at least two Dalí paintings.

The only things Edith managed to snag from her mother's deathbed were 1) the portrait of her as a small girl, trapped in a birdcage and 2) the vials of drugs that Rebekah had used to dull her pain— including antidepressants, barbiturates, and tranquilizers.

There were over 40 bottles.

Edith cherry-picked the drugs she wanted, stashed them in her bag, and told the housekeeper she had flushed them down the toilet.

Now, Angel, I'm sure Edith felt melancholy after her mother died; but, she was excited for her future. She told her sister, Terry, that she was interested in working at a suicide hotline. Edith talked about marrying her boyfriend, a nice guy, named James.

Two weeks after returning from her mother's funeral, James left town for a work trip. Edith told him to hurry back to her.

She had plans to go to a dog show with a friend the next day. She set her alarm. She poured herself a (another) glass of vodka, on the rocks.

A few minutes before seven, the maid found a few empty alcohol bottles around the house. *Edith must be drinking again,* she thought to herself.

So, the maid did what she had been told to do.

She called Edith's power of attorney: a lawyer. Her lawyer called Edith's psychiatrist, who arranged for the young woman to be admitted to the hospital. The psychiatrist and lawyer went over to Edith's house to take her themselves.

But, Edith didn't want to go.

"I've spent too much of my life in mental hospitals," the young blonde pleaded with them!

According to legend, she bargained. Edith became more and more erratic; she ran back and forth to her room. She seemed to get more and more intoxicated each time. Finally, though, Edith conceded.

"Just let me go take a shower; gather my things," Edith told the men.

That was the last time anyone saw her alive.

Edith went into her room, locked the door, and wrote a note to her boyfriend. It read:

It would take too long to explain.

Edith collapsed onto her comforter. In a trance, she opened the drawer of her bedside table. Her fingers closed around a small pill bottle: Rebekah's barbiturates.

Edith washed down the remainder of her mother's pills with an almost-empty fifth of vodka that sat next to her bed. She lit a cigarette. She closed her eyes.

Half an hour later, the doctor checked on her. Edith's bedroom door was locked. Thinking at first she had run away, the doctor tried to enter her room via the balcony. He peered in the window and saw Edith lying on her comforter motionless. A cigarette burned in her hand.

According to legend, there was another note found at the scene. Terry nor Edith's boyfriend James ever saw it. Both were suspicious about Edith's death. The medical examiner was also skeptical.

Why would this beautiful, rich young woman throw it all away?

The examiner attempted to question the men who were at Edith's home on the night she died: the psychiatrist and the lawyer.

The psychiatrist did not cooperate with the investigation. His official comment was, "Edith Harkness? Never heard of her. I know nothing about her... nothing at all. I've never even heard her name."

The lawyer, who was in charge of Edith's $10 million estate, also refused to talk about her death. The case was soon closed; ruled a suicide.

With Edith's unexpected death, the tragic remainder of the Harkness legacy was placed in the hands of Terry.

Your mother, Angel.

Terry, Bill's step-daughter... who wasn't even a real Harkness.

Life's funny like that.

Terry was devastated by the deaths of her mother and her sister; suspicious of everyone's motives. She was especially skeptical of Edith's death being ruled a suicide.

But, Terry never was able to do anything about it.

Once upon a time, long before Betty West became Rebekah Harkness, Terry Anne was her mother's favorite thing in the entire world. When Terry was young, Betty saw fragments of herself in her daughter: dark features, a round face, and a free spirit.

Things changed when Betty left Terry's father, Charles. The young girl felt lost for almost an entire year. But, then, Bill Harkness waltzed into Betty's life. He soon became a steady force in Terry's.

When Terry first met Uncle Bill, he dazzled her. Bill's presence was much needed following her parents' divorce. Motherhood was clearly not Betty's strong suit. Terry often felt neglected.

Uncle Bill, however, gave Terry genuine attention. He asked her questions about her day. Sometimes, Bill would get down on the floor to play with her. He bought her incredible toys— like a beautiful china doll that he picked up on a work trip in India and a Morse Code telegraph learning set. He left her secret messages:

.. / .-.. --- ...- . / -.-- --- ..-

(I love you)

When Bill died, Terry's life changed drastically. Her mother became distant, obsessed with her work, and distracted by all the pixies and loonies flitting around. The nannies all but took over. The children were miserable.

Eventually, enough was enough for Terry.

When she was 18, Terry packed up her things (and the relatively small inheritance Bill had left her) and moved to Malibu. Her days were spent strolling the sandy shore at Zuma Beach, flirting with surfer boys, and painting the vivid, evergreen landscape.

Most days were hotter than Hades. But, on the day she met Tony— a tall, blonde surfer boy— the sun had hidden itself behind the clouds. The salt air had taken a slight chill. It was foggy.

That day, Terry and Tony sparked a hot-and-heavy relationship in an abandoned Zuma lifeguard tower. An accident that involved a broken condom soon led to a shotgun wedding.

Your parents were young, Angel. They were free-spirited. Their marriage was rocky.

Tony became distant. He became obsessed with fasting and spent the majority of his time out of the house. Terry was unhappily married, pregnant, and largely alone.

With no one else to turn to, Terry began to rekindle her relationship with her mother. They spoke on the phone daily. Terry shared her pregnancy troubles. Rebekah shared her apprehensive excitement about becoming a grandmother.

Suddenly, it felt to Terry as if her mother actually wanted to be her friend. *This child will connect us,* Terry thought. Both women were giddy with hope for the future.

A month before the baby came, Terry and Tony got divorced. He didn't come to the hospital to wipe Terry's sweat during delivery; he didn't care to see his daughter's journey into the world.

Terry managed the delivery process alone, like a champ. Rebekah waited in the hospital's lobby.

When you were born, Angel, the first thing Terry did was check your ears... to make sure they didn't stick out. Rebekah told her to do that.

"A Harkness grandchild can not have ears like Dumbo," Rebekah coached her, before Terry was wheeled into the delivery room.

Terry soon realized that your ears were the least of her problems, Angel. You were a beautiful baby, of course... but inside of your brain, something was terribly wrong.

At first, your mother didn't notice anything abnormal. You really did look like an angel. But, then she noticed how your eyes roam. You didn't respond to your mother's voice. Eventually, Terry took you to the doctor. You were diagnosed with severe neurological damage: septooptic dysplasia syndrome."

The two hemispheres of Angel's brain weren't connected. She was blind, suffered from frequent seizures, and the entire left side of her body was useless due to spastic hemiplegia. Each day was a life or death struggle.

"Nobody knew what to do with you, my dear; your medical situation was so complex. Someone suggested we put you in a home for disabled children. Terry suggested, "Have the doctors just put the child out of her misery."

Your grandmother wouldn't hear of it.

This baby is my second chance for a legacy, Rebekah thought.

But, taking care of you was far more difficult than anyone imagined, Angel. You didn't eat very well; you couldn't even latch your lips around a bottle's nipple. You didn't hit the language milestones you were supposed to. You never figured out how to crawl.

On November 13th– the day Rebekah hired me— you were so sick, Angel. You were vomiting non-stop. You hadn't eaten in days. The doctors told me that you were't expected to live more than a few days.

But then, I stepped in. I managed to feed you. You took to me.

I remember one doctor saying, "If you take this baby, Miss Weeks, you must not leave her. She has to have a rock to cling to. If you leave her, she will die."

You know what, Angel?

I've been by your side every day since.

Rebekah doted on you, at first. She showered you with the attention she had never shown her own children. Despite your brain damage, you looked like a normal child.

But, as you grew— and your differences became more pronounced— Rebekah became more and more distant. As soon as she realized that you were never going to be the ballerina she dreamt of, she almost never visited us anymore. Neither did Terry.

Back then, though, at least they still paid our bills.

While we hunkered down in Watch Hill, Terry hopped around from sunny destination to sunny destination, desperately searching for a city (and man) to anchor herself.

She found the city in beautiful Palm Springs. She found the man in the desert, too... in a guy with Omar Sharif charm, a silky black mustache, and wavy hair that flowed back, like a mane. His name? The Wolf.

Everyone in the family hated The Wolf... including Rebekah, who met him on her death bed. Rebekah told me that, when The Wolf shook her hand for the first time, a death-like chill went down her spine.

He was pretty creepy, Angel.

The Wolf and Terry's 25-year-long, off-again-on-again relationship was tumultuous. By the time Terry was diagnosed with late-stage breast cancer, she and The Wolf were divorced. But, when she told him of her cancer diagnosis, he came running back to her. Again.

The Wolf helped Terry decide to refuse chemotherapy. She opted, instead, for alternative treatments, such as a vitamin C drip... that The Wolf took with her as a 'show of companionship.'

Terry's condition slowly worsened. She was dying. Terry knew it. Her doctors knew it. She just wanted to be comfortable.

Terry heard the nurses talking around her, but could only make out bits and pieces:

Hospice, they whispered. *Poor thing, all alone.*

Terry was admitted. Her hospice room was magnificent. The ceilings and walls were made of bamboo. If you stared at them long enough, one couldn't be clear where the wall stopped and the ceiling began. In the corner, a stone waterfall trickled, providing peaceful, ambient noise.

She had been in hospice for just a few days when The Wolf came to visit. The hospice staff had Terry taking a lot of painkillers. He noticed that she was pretty doped up.

Two days later, The Wolf and Terry wed. Her estate-planning attorney performed the bedside ceremony. No family members or other friends were present. No photos or videos of the ceremony were taken. Three days after the wedding, Terry passed away.

She died all alone.

After she died, the original beneficiaries of Terry's will — who anticipated a large share of her fortune— were surprised to learn that Terry had signed a new will, mere days before her death. The new will made The Wolf the primary beneficiary of her multi-million dollar estate.

The Wolf used the Harkness fortune to purchase a sprawling estate in Palm Springs. Over the years, law enforcement has become familiar with his fenced fortress. It has been the scene of several suspicious overdoses and 'accidental deaths.' Suddenly, headlines focus on him.

A recent one read:

The Wolf of Palm Springs:
Predator of the Addicts

Despite the suspicious circumstances of these deaths, law enforcement wrapped up all investigations— quickly and quietly. In the end, The Wolf emerged the real winner of the Harkness family's fairytale... and according to legend, he lived happily ever after."

❖

CHAPTER 18

PARADOX

"It was the best of times, it was the worst of times; it was the age of wisdom, it was the age of foolishness; it was the epoch of belief, it was the epoch of incredulity; it was the season of light, it was the season of darkness — in short, the period was so far like the present period, that some of its noisiest authorities insisted on it being received, for good or for evil, in the superlative degree of comparison only."

Charles Dickens

The third night of the storm, I had a dream.

In it, I was a wave off the coast. I bobbed along in the ocean. I enjoyed the warmth radiating from the sun. I moved with the salty breeze.

I basked in the views of the coast, but, I soon noticed something dreadful. The other waves in front of me were crashing against the shore.

This is a disaster! I thought, *an inevitable tragedy!*

A few moments later, another little wave came along. He introduced himself; told me his name was Morrie.

The little wave, Morrie, noticed I looked grim.

"What's wrong, my friend?!"

"Don't you see what's happening?!" I wailed, "We are all going to crash! All of us waves will be nothing! Our story ends in a tragedy!"

Morrie smiled.

He said, "No, no... Rhea, you don't understand. We aren't just waves. We are part of the wide, wild ocean."

My wave crashed against the shore.

I woke, in Watch Hill, with a start.

The birds chirped.

The sun was shining.

As I wiped the sleep from my eyes, the events that transpired over the past few days hit me.

I plugged in my phone, finally, and powered it on.

It's time to face the world, I thought.

Z had left me three voicemails. Abbe left nine.

My mom texted me thirteen times.

Call me, they all said.

I called Z first.

"Rhea!" He was breathless, "I've been worried about you. Are you okay?"

"I'm alright," I started. "I'm sorry to have left you hanging. We didn't have power here in Watch Hill. My phone was off. I spent a lot of time reading. I took time to think."

I swallowed.

"Have you seen the article?"

"I did," Z answered, quickly. "My manager did some digging. Apparently Keke's family in Calabasas owns the SPAC that Gemini is merging with. Both parties thought the merger would get more hype— and be more profitable— if our relationship was exposed. I think Keke gave the photos to her family, and her family gave them to Torò. That's why the article was written, Rhea."

I fumed; tears welled in my eyes.

I will never find anyone I can trust.

After a long pause,"Rhea... hey." Z hesitated. "Are you okay?" I couldn't speak.

"Rhea... we're going to get through this."

At that point, I started full-on bawling.

"I didn't think you could handle a relationship that was in the papers." I barely got the words out between my tears.

"One story was in the paper, Rhea. *Our* story wasn't."

I swallowed back more tears.

After a few moments... "Hey, Rhea," Z spoke. "How about you join me in Poland for a while? We can stay on my family's farm and can really get to know each other... without having to worry about outside noise. I think it's about time we start writing the real story of our relationship. What do you think?"

I was almost speechless.

"I'd love that," I managed.

I called Abbe, then my mom.

I told them of Z's invitation; that I would be accepting. I told them about some of the things I learned over the past few days.

"Something really cool happened," I told Abbe. "I figured out DaVinci's code."

"Wait, really?"

"Yeah... I think it's a number. An irrational number. The golden ratio. Phi. Rebekah led me on a hunt to find it. I'm still not entirely sure how or why." I responded. "And, it's a paradox."

"What is a paradox?" Abbe asked.

"A paradox is something that seems absurd or self-contradictory... even illogical. But when you investigate it further, it turns out to be not only logical, but true."

With my mom, I had a similar conversation.

"A paradox can help you find harmony between two seemingly opposing forces," I told her. "The *tension of opposites*." Mom giggled.

"Reminds me of Harmonía and her necklace."

Mom's words transported me back to my twin-sized bed at the Christmas tree farm. I could picture, in my mind's eye, a younger version of Mom sitting next to me on my quilted comforter. She whispered the story of my family's namesake: Harmonía.

The story of Harmonía begins like many others... upon Mt. Olympus. It starts with her mother, the beautiful, irrational goddess of love, Aphrodite.

Once upon a time— I believe it was on a Tuesday— a shimmering, golden goddess emerged from the foamy sea. It was Aphrodite. Her incomparable beauty and unmatched charm enchanted mortals and gods alike.

But poor, beautiful Aphrodite was blind to all of that. She was ruled by her passion; she yearned for love. *True love*... but really, anything resembling love would do.

Aphrodite thought she found love when she felt passion. So, she chased men until she found the ones who made her feel *on fire*. When she didn't have someone— or something— who sparked that burning intensity, Aphrodite felt empty. As if her passion was controlled by the same forces behind gravity, Aphrodite felt herself being involuntarily pulled towards the pursuit.

Chaos often ensued.

Many saw Aphrodite as a nymphomaniac... but, passion wasn't just about sexual desire for her. Aphrodite felt passion as a sense of movement; illustrated in the spiraling galaxies of her eyes, the crest and fall of waves in the lakes she bathed in, and the twinkling songs she crooned.

Passion, to Aphrodite, was found in *living*.

In life itself.

Many called her vain, and it may have been true. Aphrodite couldn't pass a body of water without stopping to gaze at her reflection. Beneath the stars, she painted pictures of herself in the sky.

But when Aphrodite looked at herself in the lake, she didn't see a beautiful goddess.

She saw the universe.

The dreamscapes Aphrodite painted in the sky were not of her earthly figures; they were of her essence, her spirit.

When Aphrodite pictured herself in the cosmos, she didn't see her many mortal flaws. She saw her purest self.

She saw irrational love.

At first Aphrodite was celebrated amongst the gods. She arrived to the party on a golden chariot, pulled by two winged horses. One was named Yin; the other, Yang. All of the gods flocked to Aphrodite's side because she was the most dazzling, magnificent, sparkly goddess of them all.

The male gods, especially, wanted to be near her. Aphrodite gave off the most beautiful energy. She was the life of the party. She made love day and night, with reckless abandonment. Who with? It didn't matter... nor did it matter their marital status.

Attention made Aphrodite feel invigorated. She often felt herself get lost in the high.

But stealing other kid's toys on the playground doesn't make you many friends. In fact, Aphrodite started attracting enemies.

Aphrodite lost control of her desires. She broke up marriages and drove others to madness. People either hated her or loved her; there was no in-between. In relationships, she was unable to find harmony.

Even after she was forced to marry Heph, Aphrodite couldn't be tamed. She found herself yearning for more. Soon, she was trapped in an insidious love affair. On top of her marriage with Heph, mind you!

Even more scandalous, this affair was between brothers: Ares (the god of war) and Apollo (the sun god)! Aphrodite felt pulled to each with equal intensity, as if the brothers were opposite, but infinitely increasing, forces.

Two sides of the same coin: volatility vs. balance.

Apollo and Aphrodite became very close; as did Aphrodite and Ares.

Apollo was the god of the Sun, music, light, poetry, and prophecy. Through his force, he was able to heal others. There were rumors that Apollo could see the future. According to legend, he was the one who delivered prophecies to the Oracle at Delphi.

Aphrodite was drawn to Apollo's light and knowledge. She was attracted by his impressive force.

Ares, on the other hand, was the god of political war and physical battle; order and rebellion; courage and fear. His force was so powerful, he was known by the other gods as *Raging Ares*.

Ares took pleasure in the dark side of life... some might even say he was evil. He enjoyed watching wars as they played out; he took pleasure in counting the dead.

Aphrodite was equally drawn to both brothers. But, something about Ares really tickled her fancy. She was fascinated by the unknown. The storms he created made her life feel more exciting.

Ultimately, Aphrodite's passion for Ares won out; his volatility reigned her in. By some miracle, together they created a beautiful baby girl. Harmonía.

After Aphrodite was sent to Earth— to slither around as a snake for eternity with Ares— their daughter, Harmonía was locked away in a tower like Rapunzel.

Even as a small child, Harmonía was the epitome of balance. She found love and harmony with everything she encountered: birds and snakes, alike. Animals, and the characters in her books, were her only friends.

Harmonía was finally allowed to emerge into the world when Zeus offered her up to be betrothed to Cadmus of Thebes— a mortal King with whom Zeus needed to make amends.

Anyone who was anyone— god and mortal alike— attended the wedding of Harmonía and Cadmus. It was a momentous occasion. In fact, it was the last time gods and mortals ever shared a meal together.

Even Heph, Aphrodite's ex-husband, was there.

At the wedding, Heph gave Harmonía a gift: a necklace that contained the knowledge of immortality, and symbolized the essence of beauty on Earth.

The necklace was the most beautiful thing Harmonía had ever seen; it was designed using phi in every ratio and detail. Heph told Harmonía, "Make this a family heirloom. As the necklace is passed down, it will bring its wearer eternal youth and beauty."

Many others were jealous.

Soon after the wedding, the necklace was stolen from Harmonía. She was devastated. Heph was devastated.

His plan didn't work.

The necklace Heph designed was beautiful, but it was a paradox. Heph's real intention behind the gift was to place a generational curse on Harmonía... as payback for the humiliation her parents, Aphrodite and Ares, caused him all those years ago.

Heph knew that the necklace's essence was addictive. He had a premonition: the necklace would teach its owners that value is only found in youth and beauty. That is how he could have ensured that the story of all of Aphrodite's heirs would end in tragedy. The ultimate payback.

Over the years, hundreds of explorers have searched high and low for Harmonía's stolen necklace. Some call it the philosopher's stone. Others, the *Holy Grail*.

But, I know a secret. The mystical powers of Harmonía's necklace came not from the metals and stones it was made of... rather, the knowledge the necklace symbolized: of balance and infinity.

Opposite sides of the same, irrational coin.

It is said that the stories of Greek gods make up the archetypes of human-kind. These characters live within us all. Myths comprise the universal elements of human experience... they tell the truths found at the very essence of being.

Myths are not a primitive proto-science. They are the opposite side of a traditional, rational, empirical way of thought. They are the potential of the universe in us all.

Myths seem irrational. But, maybe our lack of appreciation for them stems from modern philosophical ignorance rather than ancestral error.

Myths teach us the patterns of being. They illuminate our potential, for better and for worse. They remind us that there are two sides to every coin. They teach us that life's pain is only worth it, if you are writing your own story.

Oh, that reminds me.

The pandemic hit while I was overseas at Z's family's farm. Abbe, a speech therapist at a nursing home, went to work throughout.

She often FaceTimed me, after work. Crying.

"You're a hero!" I consoled her.

"I'm no hero. I'm broken, I'm hurting," she said. "Our flimsy PPE makes a great straitjacket. I feel like I have no control over my destiny!"

Abbe made it through a year of tragedy. She helped patients FaceTime with their families, often for the last time. She counted as nineteen of her long-term patients succumbed to the virus. As the pandemic became an epidemic, she decided to leave the medical world behind.

She spent her extra time in isolation learning about how the golden ratio and phi applies to the stock market. She used the Elliot Wave Principle[21] to help her make predictions about the price movement of stocks... and eventually hit it big, against cheating hedge funds, on a short squeeze.

Abbe doesn't know if she will ever have to work again. That's why I started writing down Rebekah's story. As a love letter to my dear friend, Abbe... and, a warning.

With great wealth comes great responsibility.

"What stock was it?" I remember asking her, incredulously. She smiled at me, like a Cheshire cat.

"GameStop."

It's quiet here. Hydrangeas cover my feet. As summer slipped

---

[21] The Elliot Wave Principle is a form of technical analysis that traders use to predict market cycles and trends. It paints a picture of human psychology. The golden ratio is a major component.

away, I watched my surroundings transform from snow white to pinkish-orange.

Leaves fall. The sun almost always shines and there are plenty of trees for shade. From the little library down the street, I got a library card. That card is the key to some of time's best stories.

When I came home from Poland, I bought a cottage in up-state New York. It isn't much, but it has the most beautiful garden.

Z and I spend a lot of time here.

I'm writing this from a little bench in the corner of that garden. We're nestled on a big plot of land... tucked away, where no one can ever find me.

A seat on the outside of life's bigger narratives seemed almost unattainable, especially for me. But I've come to understand that stories just bring drama. Time brings tragedy.

I'm so tired of grieving.

You live, and you learn. Then you live some more and learn some more. This story repeats, over and over.

What would happen if every moment of your life was reduced to just data points— a measure of your reality versus optimal self, graphed on a scatter plot across time?

You would hope to see a steady trend upwards throughout your life. Any upwards spikes may be followed by a downwards trend, and then a swift recovery back to right around equilibrium. You would, hopefully, keep trending upwards until you die and your story (apparently) ends.

Your story doesn't end when you die, though. When you die, your reality may cease to be... but, your legacy doesn't. Each time someone whispers your name, sings your song, or tells your story... your legacy lives on.

In this way your little data points wouldn't show a trend that abruptly ceases to be. Your graph is so much bigger. The story of the world is so much bigger.

Think about people like Keats, Kennedy, Hardin, Ginsburg, the volunteer school board member, or a COVID nurse. Death was just a blip on the overall trend of their scatterplot. Their stories will continue to trend on. Upwards?

In the greater tragedy, though, who will get casted for which role? What about when the next story starts? One that is even more dramatic. Then the next one?

Hunny, it's turtles all the way down.

For those who are lucky enough, the seeds of their legacy are watered and tended to across time, by family members, people in the community, or fans of their work.

Some's seeds never bloom. Some need better soil and the right gardener to pick the weeds and nourish their seeds. Maybe any spirit can be gardened back to life.

Time is this wondrous thing.

I'll never know when my story is going to end— or even what part of which chapter I'm currently on.

All I know is that I want my story to be about love, courage, and positivity. I want to prove— to myself and every other person— that *anyone* can be the hero, both in their personal stories and in life's most important stories.

How?

Seek to trend near your equilibrium. Stand up only when the time is right. Aim to raise your trend, but never let it go parabolic.

Remember Newton's Law. Find a way to trend above your tormentors and never fall into the real tragedy of life: playing the victim.

Always remember: what you believe, you are.

I've had purple-pink skies for many of life's sunsets. But, twilight is inevitably followed by the dark of night. Balance is the key to finding true happiness.

I've learned that I can't control the rumors on the street. I can't control what the headlines scream. I can't control what people tweet at me, what they do with my music, or what they say about me. I can't control how people think about me, view me, or love me.

I can work towards balance... towards maintaining an upwards trending equilibrium. I can trust that some people love me for me... and that they won't be influenced by outside noise. I can learn, and love, and learn, and love... until my dying day.

I realized that I do have control of what I put out into the world. So, I'm going to construct the best of what my heart has to offer, while I still can.

I can control my attitude... and never forget that my reality is just my own, flawed, perception. I control who I let in and what experiences I let in.

I can remember that it is best to trend right around equilibrium. I'll strike upwards. But, only when the time is right... or when it is in love.

It is fitting here, to quote one of my favorite, fellow pop-stars— who, funny enough, was born in 1989 (just about nine months after Dalí died).

I want to still have a sharp pen, a thin skin, and an open heart.

Love is life, and life is love. The most important thing in the whole world is love— real love. Irrational love. The type of love that, upon calculation, might equal a transcendent, infinite, irrational number.

Phi.

Some people find that kind of love with only one person in their lives, others more. I've learned a sad truth: the more money you have, the harder that kind of love is to find.

There are things you can do to find irrational love and transcendent balance within your own story. Be mindful. Surround yourself with people with whom you can grow in a state of equilibrium. Preserve those relationships.

When you find your people, cherish them. Adore the ones who you love, and who love you back.

Those people are your true family. Your tribe. That love is all that matters, no matter where life takes you.

Never forget that you are the author of your own story. During your life, you get to choose the stories you're a part of. Don't get distracted by other people, illustrators, or forces. Remember, you call the shots.

It's your story.

Embrace all that life brings. Allow it to change you, filter your soul, and help you grow. Be prepared for the equal and opposing forces that inevitably follow greatness.

In this kaleidoscopic world, what you believe, you are. Just remember... your story belongs to whomever is lucky enough to tell it.

CHAPTER 19

TRAGEDY

"Mostly, we swaddle ourselves in the sacrilege of self-justification and kowtow to a god we have silently rechristened ego. All things are acceptable in the all-seeing eye of self-interest. Within the walls of our flimsy Jericho, we court ruin."

Dan Johnson

The fairytale of Rebekah (Betty) West Harkness tells the story of a girl's wildest dreams coming true. Exceptionally wealthy. Extremely well-traveled. Premier patroness of the arts and ballet. An acclaimed and, at times, spectacular dance company. Lavish homes. A slew of famous friends. Many lovers. A few great loves.

Rebekah Harkness showed the world— including Jane and her late father— that the eccentric, loud, and capricious Betty West could do anything she wanted to do. She could be anyone she wanted to be.

Rebekah pursued happiness. She did what she was supposed to do: she worked hard, was self-indulgent, generous, and tried to appear interesting. Along the way, she lost sight of what was truly important. She lost sight of the things in life that bring true satisfaction.

The press humiliated her. No one took her work seriously. Her dance company folded. She lost friends. She was hoodwinked. She always put her trust in the wrong person. Her motivations seemed to be driven by childhood fantasies, rather than real artistic vision. She seemed to be incapable of discerning between real genius and the boot-licking minions always parading around.

Even in death, Rebekah's story is a tragedy.

She was cremated. Rebekah's ashes were to remain in Dali's whimsical Chalice of Life forever— her soul immortalized, just like the Egyptians. Rebekah dreamt of her gilded essence twirling and shimmering for eternity.

The chalice, however, was far too small for Rebekah's actual remains. A friend joked, "just a leg is in there... or maybe half of her head and an arm."

Terry carried the remainder of her mother's ashes home in a humble, plastic grocery bag. A few weeks later, when Rebekah's estate was liquidated, the chalice was sold to a Japanese art gallery.

At the tip of her parabolic peak, Rebekah was worth (what today would be equivalent to) almost a billion dollars. When she passed away, the majority of her fortune had dissipated in a fog of addiction: to drugs, alcohol, sex, success, and attention.

Still, Rebekah repeated her grandfather's parable, daring it to come true, "Shirtsleeves to shirtsleeves in three generations."

It wasn't just her family's story, mind you. *Shirtsleeves to shirtsleeves* is a universal cultural proverb— thought to exist within all groups of people and all written languages— relevant to modern and ancient times. Parables and proverbs are stories that teach fundamental truths.

The truth of this story? Wealth, like anything in life, follows an invisible pattern. It ebbs and it flows.

In the years before Rebekah died, she had almost been forgotten about completely. Once a ruckus-causing debutante, then daring socialite, then eccentric heiress… finally, a ghost.

The prestige of the Harkness family name— once associated with wealth and success— had nose-dived. In some circles, people mentioned the name Rebekah Harkness, but only with a smirk or as part of a cautionary tale.

Rebekah's rise was meteoric. She made her dreams come true. But, she fell... as people often do. When she toppled, she crashed head-first into the pavement. Rebekah dragged the other stories tangled in her web down with her.

The Last Great American Dynasty:
the esteemed Harkness name and
Standard Oil Fortune destroyed!

Poor Little Princess!
Edith commits suicide with pills stolen
from her mother's death bed!

Deathbed Wedding:
The Wolf steals away with millions from his doped up
ex-wife... an heiress with only days to live.

A trinity of tragedies marks the end of Rebekah's fairytale and your family's dynasty, Angel. The choices that Rebekah made throughout her life created a ripple effect that have outlasted her physical presence on Earth.

Looking back it's no wonder... chaos and volatility were her legacy. Now, the Harkness legacy (and fortune) belong to the wolves.

Maybe the downfall of Rebekah Harkness was the true tragedy of the *American Dream,* Angel. Her demise seems to be inevitable.

It turns out that life is only fun when you're living for the hope of it all. Once the dream comes true, it becomes a nightmare."

Miss Weeks was utterly exhausted. She stood, quietly closed the girl's door, and started the ascent towards her own room.

As she passed her favorite reading alcove, she peered out the paned window at the full moon.

The sky was clear. The man on the moon was smiling. Miss Weeks could see his reflection on the still, salty water.

Still, she was not at peace.

Angel could never have understood the story told tonight; but, maybe the girl was the right person to tell.

Chaos seems to be contagious. As it bubbled inside of Miss Weeks, the nanny felt as if she was going to burst.

The nanny had seen the same story play out one too many times.

She was beginning to realize how synchronistic the tragedy was. She watched, helpless, as it repeated generation after generation and with empire after empire.

Maybe Miss Weeks just needed to talk about it. You know, I've found talking to be helpful— both to remember and forget.

The nanny had been puzzling the pieces together. She was beginning to understand that the very idea of the *American Dream* was but another rendition of the *shirtsleeves to shirtsleeves* parable playing out in real-time and in a spectacular fashion.

The story is universal; one that has perfectly described rational human nature throughout time, within every culture, and across all social hierarchies:

Clogs to clogs.

From stalls, to stars, back to stalls.

The rich get richer… until the tides inevitably turn.

Shirtsleeves to shirtsleeves is the story of generational wealth: the father buys, the son builds, the grandchild sells, and his son begs. Wealth gained by one generation will be lost by the third. Time after time— as evidenced with generation after generation— even the most massive of fortunes are drained by those who follow. Both on individual and grander scales.

The first generation usually starts without wealth and possibly without education. But, they know the recipe for success: work hard, become an entrepreneur, protect yourself, and set your family up for the future.

This first generation goes to work in shirtsleeves. Their main focus is to foster a better life for their children... maybe even for their children's children.

Someday, they think, *someone in my family tree will have the freedom to live their best life.*

The next generation becomes lawyers, engineers, CEOs, and doctors. They enjoy traveling the world and indulge in modern-day luxuries. The parents walked to work in shirtsleeves and now, the children drive to work in a suit and a tie. The suit-and-tie generation saw the sacrifices the previous generations made to amass the family fortune.

But, then the third generation is raised with all the spoils of wealth. Children in this pampered generation don't get to experience— or even hear a first-hand account— of the hard work and sacrifice it took for their family to get to this level. This generation only hears the stories.

But, stories change over the time. They may become more relatable, or less; more meaningful, or less.

This third generation almost always demonstrates lavish consumption of the family fortune... and the story seems to end in inevitable tragedy. Then, the fourth generation goes back to work in shirtsleeves.

How does this relate to the *American Dream*?

The general notion of the *American Dream* is the belief that anyone can become exceedingly successful— through the pioneer virtues of hard work, perseverance, ingenuity, and fortitude— and that one might find happiness through wealth. In America, each man and woman has an equal opportunity to become richer and better.

With this dogma, no external forces matter. This story accounts for no bouts of luck. All one needs is a chip on their shoulder, a touch of grit, and excellent work ethic... then, they can have the success and bliss— the life— they've always wanted.

"If you can't make the dream work for you?" They sneer, "Well, then there is something wrong with you!"

They cry, "Maybe it's because you aren't smart enough! Maybe, you aren't working hard enough! Maybe, you just aren't that valuable!"

Either way, "We all deserve what we get."

That may be true.

Still, we all follow the shimmering paths towards the *American Dream* in an axiomatic fashion; blindly and without questioning. But, the dream everyone is working towards appears to be a collective drama.

Appearing next month, off-Broadway: *The Tragedy of the Commons*. Here's a quick summary:

Picture a pasture open to all (the commons).

It is to be expected that each herdsman will try to keep as many cattle as possible in the commons.
The rational herdsman concludes that the only sensible course of action for him to pursue, is to add another animal to his herd... then another, and another, and another.
This is the conclusion reached by each and every rational herdsman sharing a commons.

Therein lies the tragedy.

Therein lies the tragedy.

Each rational man is caged by a system that compels him to increase his herd without limit— despite living on an earth that has limited resources. Freedom of the commons encourages rational humans to pursue their own best interest, no matter the cost.

When economic and political development rests upon the unquestioned dogma of pursuing limitless growth, freedom of the commons brings ruin to all.

History has made it clear. Any 'rational' story abides by social Darwinism: *eat or be eaten, grow or die.*

It seems that we are all locked in a system that compels us to increase our wealth without limit. That system is just one of the many invisible cages that trap us. Blindly running away on our hamster wheels, we don't realize that most are just living as the means to another's end.

It's no accident that the term tragedy was chosen to articulate the fate of the commons.

What makes a tragedy? Grief. Drama.

The realization that anyone, and thus everyone, would likely have acted in a similar way? The realization that anyone— even you— may have met the same dreadful, inevitable end?

A tragedy doesn't involve epic suspense. It needs not just a calamitous outcome. It doesn't make the audience feel pity, in the sense that random chance has dealt the character a bad hand.

Essential to tragedy is rationality.

The soul of the tragedy lies in cognitive dissonance; of the reader having some foreboding knowledge about the inevitably of the ending. The essence of a tragedy is the recognition that rationality itself is what permitted the inevitable.

Things could never have been otherwise.

In our own lives we gloss over the painful truth, but tragedy satisfies a fundamental need to face up to it. Our pleasure in the drama is precisely that of learning those hard lessons— in understanding the universal truths about our predicament and the nature and causes of human suffering.

The good news? In life's drama, you get to choose the role you want to play. But, beware: good is just one *rational* choice from evil.

CHAPTER 20

RENAISSANCE

"The purpose of life, as far as I can tell... is to find a mode of being that's so meaningful that the fact that life's suffering is no longer relevant."

Jordan Peterson

Limitless growth, expansion, potential: I am living proof of the *American Dream*.

Rae Harmonía— America's Favorite Pop-star— went from a small Christmas tree farm in Pennsylvania to making millions by the time she was eighteen.

One day she was belting tunes on the stage of her community's theatre; the next, she was singing a *Don't Stop Believing* duet with the the future King of England. She glided around the world in a private jet, hopped from luxurious castle to penthouse apartment, partied with models, and dated actors and billionaires.

Mine seems to be a story that anyone would want.

A fairytale, even.

It is true. I am what my family— what many of our families— have been working towards for generations.

In their stories, these dogmas repeat:

Eat or be eaten. Grow or die.
Money will solve your problems.
Success is the key to happiness.

But upon arguably the tallest peak of life's highest mountain, having found all the success and money I ever dreamed of, I looked around and didn't find happiness.

Instead, I found myself an addict. I sought volatility... longed for the high. I was hooked on feeling *special.*

I'd do anything— sacrifice my own well-being, even— to keep people entertained. To dazzle a crowd. To be *good.*

But, specialness doesn't come cheap.

As I recognized the parallels between the stories of Rebekah and myself, I realized that she wasn't just pursuing happiness. On the contrary. She— just like many other artists, creatives, innovators, visionaries, and thinkers that came before (alongside and after) her— pursued feeling sparkly.

I saw that same story repeat in my own life, with my friends, and especially in the stories of my fellow entertainers. I read about it in books... over and over and over.

Hell, the paradox of success has been a battle in the psyche of even myth's greatest heroes. Like Achilles, for example, who chose certain death in the Trojan War over a long life with his loved ones at home.

For him, the only way was to die at a peak.

But, isn't that a tragedy?

It was only when my mirrorball was shattered on the floor, and I thought the life and legacy of America's Most Promiscuous Pop-star had no hope of a prosperous future, that I came to two disturbing conclusions:

1) When pursuing success, unless we die a tragic death like Achilles, we will never be satisfied.
2) The story most rational people are living is an epic tragedy.

That story is the tragedy of the *American Dream*— a culture that glorifies overwork and crawls with addicts always feening for *more*. It is the tragedy of the commons— of rationality to the system, not the universe. It is the tragedy of the industrial revolution: injustice, climate change, and laissez-faire capitalism. It is the tragedy of the technological revolution: automation, social media, and instant, limitless information.

It's the tragedy of modern times.

It's the tragedy of truth decay— of working more and thinking less. It's the tragedy of a mainstream media (and collective news source) that is owned and operated by the rich. It's the tragedy of Pinnochio: a puppet, controlled by invisible strings.

It's the tragedy of a loss of collective wisdom. It's the tragedy of negativity, polarization, and of not wanting to confront difficult things that matter. It's the tragedy of humankind getting further away from equilibrium: a paramount place of transcendent, harmonious truth.

The collective has become addicted to dogma over reflection; defense over curiosity; blame over mindfulness and self-correction; rationality over everything else.

I've heard it said, *when ignorance destroys culture, monsters inevitably emerge.*

But, my dear reader, what if we've just been storying the *American Dream* all wrong?

What if we've been storying our lives all wrong?

Maybe the enlightened human shouldn't simply seek to be rational, but hyper-rational. Irrational, even.

Each story in the universe ebbs and flows in parallel fashion to the ones in our lives.

As you become more mindful, you'll see stories repeat.

You'll notice synchronicities appear.

There have been chapters when history should not have allowed the enlightenment of people. But even in the Dark Ages, people fought for the light... through knowledge, philosophy, and spirit.

Once you fight your way out of the dark, you realize that the darkness was just another story. Dawn always follows. A Renaissance, even.

Maybe, the tragedy is just a paradox. Another piece of the puzzle that can bring us closer to unlocking humankind's most fundamental question— how should one live?

Chance and necessity play a prominent, and often devastating, role in our lives. So, it may only be through tragedy, the very question— how should we live?— acquires its true urgency and complexity.

But, here's the thing about tragedies... according to Aristotle, within the drama, there must be nothing irrational.

If the irrational cannot be excluded from the story, it is *outside the scope of a tragedy*. If one uncovers an element that is irrational... well, the story can't be a tragedy!

Found in the cosmos, phi is logical proof of irrationality. Phi tells us that the story of our universe isn't a tragedy. Phi might also tell us that our collective story doesn't have to be a tragedy. Our story can be *infinite*.

Irrationality is the most logical piece of evidence to suggest that our fate will only be the *tragedy of the commons,* if that is the story we collectively write.

As I sat alone in my garden I came to this realization: the *American Dream* isn't about capitalism, success, nor the pursuit of happiness.

The unforgettable story of the *American Dream* captures the essence of humanity. It is the story of adventurers who dreamed, dared, and accomplished. The story of curiosity, cleverness, and luck. It is the story of innovators, brave enough to write their own stories.

Through their stories, I've learned that human beings have infinite possibilities on Earth. There is no need to simply tolerate life. We each have the power to write our own beautiful story... and, in turn, become anyone we want to be.

The *American Dream* is just a symbol of irrational opportunity. It shows that anyone has the ability to write their own story; to create their own order in the chaos.

Are we this lucky by chance or by design?

Free will or fate? Is there a difference?

My name is Rhea Harmonía.

I'm a poet.

Poets are seekers of knowledge. They are philosophers. They are story tellers. They create art that inspires people to ask deeper questions about the stories that make up collective reality.

Poets puzzle words together, which in turn, transforms potential into actuality. Words help create order in chaos.

Things come into being when there is a fire that sparks their potential. Any kind of transformation is possible with a simple exchange of energy. This energy exchange can be as easy as listening to the music written by your favorite pop-star, or reading a book by your favorite author.

Alone in my garden, I also realized that I couldn't simply aim to be excluded from the narrative. One can never be truly excluded from the universe's story and feel whole.

A narrative is woven throughout all of us: the threads of our collective soul. In order to find true happiness, I understand that I need to accept my part in the story of the collective. I need to understand how my part relates to the whole.

I used DaVinci's code to find the answers. Phi is part of the puzzle that tells us the dark ages have lingered. An age of divide is being manifested. We need a Renaissance; we need collective enlightenment.

Philosophers enlighten and create order through stories, which help them confront the unknown, voluntarily. Philosophers often become poets. They tell stories so that the darkness (when it inevitably comes) doesn't destroy them completely.

Maybe we all tell stories as an attempt to escape the inevitable.

I've learned that— as long as you understand the story's beginning and use creativity to fill the gaps— when you write a different conclusion, the entire story changes.

Poets are like a phoenix— a bird that can die and be reborn forever. Just like a phoenix, a poet must voluntarily allow their ego to die and regenerate. They often learn painfully and through tragic circumstance.

For a poet, experience always destroys previous certainty with new and more complete knowledge. This transformation may only be possible through storying the chaos when tragedies emerge.

Poets know how to turn tragedies into lessons. They create myths. Often, through the creative process, the poet becomes a myth themselves.

Mythological figures live many lives and die many deaths. They differ in this way from characters in most novels... characters that are two-dimensional and have no true form outside the page.

Characters in myths are omni-present, in a way that we see their patterns repeat— through their stories, our lives, and all of history. Through myth, we can identify the archetypes of all being.

Myths are a paradox, in and of themselves. In the mythological world, anything can be one thing and its opposite at the same time. This often happens in direct opposition to an objective, rational viewpoint.

When Rhea, the mother of Zeus, saved him from an awful fate of being swallowed alive, she broke a cycle of tragedy. When she did, she entered another story… the story of modern times.

Maybe the key to understanding that story is through the story of Harmonía, the bastard child of love and war. Her story is the true tension of opposites... but it was never about good or bad.

The key to understanding is found through alignment. It's about the unity you feel when you are One with the universe. It's the harmony you feel when you are listening to a damn good song.

Harmony perpetuates the cyclical nature of life and creativity. With any innovation, new myths are formed.

Poems (and song-lyrics) are a rare form in which stories can be passed down; a medium that the listener can use to abduct meaning for themselves.

I've been thinking... maybe the collective doesn't know they're supposed to abduct. That type of critical thinking is no longer explicitly taught in mainstream education.

As a society, we're at a crossroads: the place you meet the devil. We whine, "Life is chaotic. Nothing has meaning."

But, something is missing.

Logos.

Logos is the human capacity for consciousness and communication. It is our reason for existence; the patterns of meaning. Logos is speaking the truth. It is having discussions about the irrational nature of our universe. It is generating solutions to collective problems. Logos is the path we discover as we go through the world and paint our own story.

Logos teaches us that the whole is greater than the sum of its parts; also, that the true nature of something's parts is always determined by its relation to the whole.

Logos can be scary.

Infinity is chaotic.

Irrationality can be dangerous.

It has driven men to kill; it has driven women mad. But, I think the irrational is only dangerous when it is kept a secret... when the truth is hidden away, out of sight and out of mind. It is only dangerous when we don't talk about it.

See, irrationality isn't just chaos. The other side of the coin is the transcendent potential required to find universal order. Harmony. The logos of relation can show us how each part of the universe has its place in the fabric of the whole.

Luckily, a Renaissance is here; the real Age of Enlightenment. Now, everyone has the tools needed to create a meaningful life.

It turns out, all we need— all we ever needed— has been hiding in plain sight, buried in the depths of our favorite things.

Logos.

Logos can be found in poetry, literature, films, art, architecture... music. Logos can be found in the irrational; in pure, transcendent love.

Logos can be found inside yourself.

Well, the cat is out of the bag.

The age of information has exposed the secret of the Ancient Egyptians and Pythagoreans to the world. You, now, know their paradoxical, irrational secret.

Do with it what you will.

Cry about it. Forget it. Pass it down.

Create with it. Learn from it. Let it change you.

Just don't say you never heard the story… because, now you have.

Maybe one day you can tell your children, "We are the lucky ones. Our existence is **not** a tragedy. We are fragments of a mystical, infinite creation."

I may soothe mine to sleep with this:

Here is the universe, little one.
It is beautiful and tragic.
Embrace it. Enjoy it. Do not be afraid.
Listen close. Find the patterns. Learn to love.

Once you know real love,
you may begin to understand The One.
Only then, can you be whole.

CODA

This book was written during the months of September 2020– April 2021 as a creative outlet during the pandemic. All aspects of *Lucky's* creation were handled by me, Kristina Parro, and my newly established company Logos LLC including: front/back cover design, formatting, developmental edits, promotion, and publishing.

First and foremost, this book would literally have not been possible without Mateusz, my Z. Thank you… for everything.

Nor would this book have been possible without Craig Unger, author of *Blue Blood.* I spent countless hours studying both the material he compiled and his writing style. I became a better writer and story teller for it. Thank you. Gratitude is also directed at the Newberry Library for allowing me access.

I'd like to express a huge amount of thanks for my editors and beta-readers, who poured hours and hours into this book and helped me make it what it is today. A special thank you to Caitlyn S., Sandy S., Scott B., Lizzie J., Hayley P., Sarah H., Dhwani P., Alyssa S., Rae S., Keniel O., and of course, my mom. Thanks to the following people who have also been of assistance to me during this process: my brother, Joe C., Aleen O., Larry F., Grace C., April and Nick, Bryan, Teresa Z., Damian Z., and my dad.

Thank you to Carl R., Brandie V., and Aleen O. for making an awesome photo shoot happen (front and back cover photography) and Om N., my amazing illustrator, who made my visions come to life!

Follow Om on Instagram!! @a.merry.gold.owl

Thanks to all of my family and friends (old and new) who have supported me in this endeavor. It's great to have amazing people on your team. I love you guys.

I must list my inspirations for *Lucky*. There are plenty, and this is not an exhaustive list. However, the creations and musings of these people are what I leaned on during both the pandemic and the writing of this book: Taylor Swift, Mario Livio, David Loy, Jordan Peterson, John and Hank Greene, Lin Manuel Miranda, Jason Robert Brown, Thomas King, Lana Wilson, Peter Critchley, Holly Shapiro, Mitch Albom, Farrin Chwalkowski, Erik Larson, Ava Gardner, Russel Brand, Saudamini Mishra, Matthew MacLellan, Robin Sharma, Billie Eilish and Finneas, Ralph Nelson Elliot, Elon Musk, Matthew McConaughey, Glennon Doyle, Stuart E. Lewis, Matthew Desmond, John N. Robinson, Simon J Bronner, Kate Chopin, Charolette Perkins, Dan Ariel, Ben Horowitz, Sarah Bakewell, Milton Friedman, V.E. Schwab, J.K. Rowling, Lori Gottlieb, William Wians, Renni Brown, Dave King, Eugene Wigner, Matthew Desmond, Christophe Le Mouet, Frost and Pretcher, Micheal Burry, Jens O. Parson, Keith Gill (DFV), Atobitt, Rensole, and all of the authors, poets, musicians, and thinkers mentioned throughout *Lucky*.

Finally, I must thank all of the teachers— at Wood View Elementary, Brooks Middle School, and Bolingbrook High School— professors— at Butler University and Rush University— and supervisors (work, school, volunteer, etc.) that I have had the pleasure of being taught by. Each of you has made an impact on who I am and the way I think. I am forever grateful!

I was able to gather virtually all of the information I needed for this project for free: online, and via libraries. Special thanks to the Library of Congress, Newberry Library, Fountaindale Public Library, Chicago Public Library, Standford University's Encyclopedia of Philosophy, academia.edu, and all of the marvelous YouTube channels/ blogs out there on the internet.

It's a beautiful time to be alive, y'all… especially for the curious.

Here is the universe, little one.
It is beautiful and tragic.
Embrace it. Enjoy it. Do not be afraid.
Listen close. Find the patterns. Learn to love.

Once you know real love,
you may begin to understand The One.
Only then, can you be whole.

φ

ABOUT THE AUTHOR

Lucky is Kristina Parro's debut, self-published novel. Kristina is a voracious reader who, during the pandemic, found sharing stories to be just as fun as reading them. Kristina is an alum of Butler University and Rush University. She currently lives in Chicago, IL and is a speech-language pathologist, entrepreneur (Logos LLC), investor, and lover of wisdom.

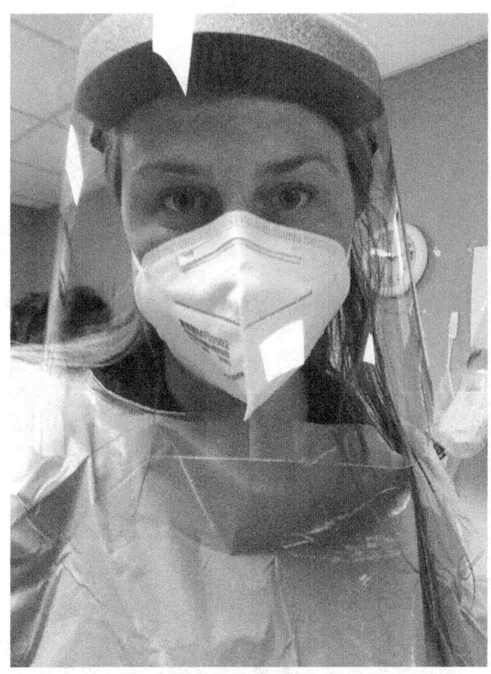

Website/Blog: KristinaParro.com

Hardcover copies: kristinaparro.myshopify.com
Paperback copies: Amazon
Ebook: Amazon and Kindle Select
Audiobook available soon— check my website for more information

Email the Author: kristina@kristinaparro.com
Business Inquiries: logos@kristinaparro.com

Instagram: @kristinaparrowrites
@logosllc

CALL TO ACTION

If you enjoyed *Lucky,* I'd love to hear about it! If you didn't, I'd also like to hear about it! Feel free to email me at kristina@kristinaparro.com. Follow me on Instagram for more *Lucky* content: @kristinaparrowrites.

Reviews are monumentally important, especially for a new author like me. It would be much appreciated if you could take a moment to write your thoughts on Amazon, Good Reads, or my website. Thank you in advance!

To generate buzz around my book and to help it compete with traditionally-published titles, it would be incredible if you could pass my book on!

How? Share it! Take pictures of/with it! Post it on social media. Gift it to someone who inspires you. Talk about it with your friends, family, neighbors, coworkers— heck, even your dog! Recommend it to your book clubs! Retire old copies to a neighborhood Little Free Library.

It's the Butterfly Effect (Chaos Theory... right, Ed?): anything you do to spread the word is helpful and appreciated.

Finally, I hope this book inspires you to take control of your story. Life is curious, magical, and wondrous. We are the lucky ones. Take advantage.

A LOGOS BOOK

AN IMPRINT OF LOGOS LLC

KRISTINAPARRO.COM

Made in the USA
Middletown, DE
19 December 2023